Carols of

Christmases Past

By Linda M. Brissett
illustrated by Ian F. Brissett

Published 1996 by:
Briss Books Inc.
Hamilton, Ontario

Canadian Cataloguing in Publication Data

Brissett, Linda M.
Carols of Christmases Past

ISBN # 0-9699369-1-5

1. Brissett, Linda M. – Childhood and youth.
2. Christmas – Jamaica. I. Title

PS8553.R547Z53 1996   C818'.5403
C96-931428-0   PR9199.3.B6938Z463 1996

Illustrations:
Ian F. Brissett

Typesetting by: Carole M. Lidgold Services

Printed and Bound in Canada by:
The AIIM Group
Aurora, Ontario

To my mother, Ada Louise, and also to my Scottish 'Family' Isabella Matheson, Joan Stewart and Agnes MacVicar.

CONTENTS

FOREWORD

In *Carols of Christmases Past*, Linda Brissett presents a wonderful, eclectic collection of stories and reflections based on the common theme of reminiscences of Christmas. Because Linda is not only a warm and cheerful person, but also someone who is contemplative and observant, she is able to weave together a rich tapestry of the diverse elements which combine to make up the Christmas season. The reader will be pleasantly surprised to find that many of these stories evoke a wide range of emotions as well as memories of momentous events and significant incidents associated with the celebration of past Christmases.

"Christmas in Jamaica", for example, brought back a flood of recollections to me. Linda's skilful description of the warmth and joy of celebrations among families and friends, and the buoyant conviviality of the festivities, struck a responsive chord.

A lighthearted look at Christmas can also be seen in "Of Christmas Cards and Rum Punch". A series of amusing events serve to remind us that "moderation in all things" is a useful maxim.

Most immigrants who go from the Caribbean to Britain or North America probably have vivid recollections of their first winter and the initial sense of alienation which they experienced. Linda recounts "My Most Memorable Christmas" with an uncanny sense of total recall. So intense is the portrayal that, reading this narration, I could almost feel the icy blast of winter.

Indeed, past Christmases are not all presented as sagas of happiness. Poignant memories of childhood are captured in "Remembering the Candy Shoppe". This story serves to remind us that life is not a series of unalloyed pleasures and that death and disaster are features of life that we all have to confront and overcome even as we grieve sudden and tragic losses. "Poinsettias and Holly" seem to emphasize this idea. Nevertheless, Linda always succeeds in striking an optimistic note. There is always a ray of sunshine behind the most gloomy and depressing clouds. "A Gift for Freddie" suggests that no calamitous situation is entirely without hope and that one should never abandon oneself to sorrow and despair.

I sense that even when the twin evils of prejudice and discrimination are examined in "Walking Against the Wind" and "Santa – the Imposter", there is nevertheless the expectation that the better parts of human nature will prevail and that inter-personal relations will improve.

In the end, Linda remains a philosopher. Her two poems plus "Christmas Is in the Heart" provide eloquent testimony of her zest for life, her belief in the noblest qualities that people possess, and her confidence that righteousness and moral excellence will always triumph.

Carols of Christmases Past is a welcome addition to our libraries.

Winston Morrison, Ph.D.

ACKNOWLEDGEMENT

I acknowledge with thanks, Ian F. Brissett for kindly doing the illustrations and Dr. Winston Morrison for reading the manuscript and writing the foreword.

INTRODUCTION

This collection of stories, articles and poems which make up the book *Carols of Christmases Past* was written with the reader's enjoyment in mind.

Some of the stories are true but are not necessarily auto-biographical.

Although *Christmas* is the theme throughout this book, there are diversities in the stories as each deals with something in particular. This could be the description of how Christmas is celebrated in a particular, tropical country as compared with a temperate one. Or the examination of feelings and perceptions of the characters and certain experiences that they have encountered which affect their enjoyment (or non-enjoyment) of Christmas, in one way or another.

The need for dignity, and the desire for fair play are things which people crave regardless of their stations in life, or their geographical habitat. I have tried to deal with these issues honestly and as gently as possible.

This book is a continuous adventure which I hope will be a source of enjoyment to you the reader, and not only at Christmas time, but throughout the year.

Linda Brissett

Christmas In Jamaica

A holiday in paradise is something most of us, at some time or other in our lives, desire. It is something some of us who are either rich or lucky, may one day get.

Paradise means different things to different people. To some, it could be doing anything, anywhere on earth. It could be relaxing at a summer cottage by the lake somewhere in Northern Ontario or Quebec; or in a condo or bungalow overlooking the sea in Florida.

It could mean owning a chalet in the Swiss Alps, where you can go skiing to your heart's content. Or a castle in Scotland, adjacent to Balmoral, and being able to play polo with Prince Charles.

My paradise happens to be on the Caribbean island of Jamaica, during the month of December, and especially Christmas week.

I am not rich, just lucky. Lucky to have been born and raised in Jamaica. Because all it takes for me to enjoy my paradise, is my airfare there and back.

For you, the not so lucky, I will give an insight into Christmas on my paradise island, as I remember it.

Christmas in Jamaica is special, not only to me the native born, but to any lucky visitor who is able to see it at its festive best.

11

At this time of year, the weather is perfect. The sun shines brightly as it always does, but there is a subtle tenderness to its warmth. The harshness of its rays which are evident in July and August, is no longer apparent, and the legendary 'Christmas Breeze' which is synonymous with December, blows gently and continuously until mid–February. This is one of the things Jamaicans who are away from their island at this time of year, yearn for with a passion as fierce as the August sun.

If a Jamaican is asked to describe the 'Christmas Breeze,' he may reply simply that it is "different," or that "it feels nice." It is very difficult to describe it to a foreigner. To me it is like sprinkling talcum over an irritating itch; or wading in the cool water by the shore, after walking barefooted across a wide expanse of hot sand.

Water sports and other activities such as golfing, cricket, and football (North American soccer), are still indulged in, but on a much lower scale.

There is a quiet excitement and expectancy in the air, and on the faces of people as they hustle to and fro.

Radios in homes and businesses, as well as juke boxes and loud speakers in stores and restaurants all over the island (no matter how remote the area), blare out the sounds of Christmas. It may be 'Jingle Bells' or 'Rudolph the Red nosed Reindeer' with a reggae beat, or 'Mary's Boy Child' calypso style. But everyone's ears (except of course the profoundly deaf), are treated liberally to festive music from December first, to the end of the month, whether they like it or not.

12

The week before Christmas, is a very busy time for all. Housewives turn their homes 'upside down.' Everything that needs to be, is washed and ironed, cleaned, dusted and aired.

Most of the homes, especially in the rural areas, have hardwood mahogany floors. These are stripped, polished and buffed until one can actually see his reflection through the shine. When I was a child, most of this polishing was done on one's hands and knees, with the help of a coconut brush fashioned for the purpose. The process took hours to complete, depending on the size of the house one was cleaning.

The living rooms, mostly those in rural areas, are decorated with varying sized bunches of grapefruits, oranges, tangerines and uglyfruits (sometimes water coconuts are thrown in as extras). Citrus fruits are chosen because they keep longer. These fruits are hung at strategic points on the walls, and are not taken down and eaten until after Boxing Day.

Candles in decorative colours were once used as Christmas lights, but because of the risk of fires, they are now being discouraged.

Pieces of foil from cigarette cartons, collected over a period of months, make humble, but effective angels and stars, to decorate many rural homes; and crepe paper, tinsel and balloons add the finishing touch. In modern times and homes, especially in cities, North American style decorations are widely used. These are mostly purchased abroad by holidaying islanders, or sent by relatives living in North America. But though such decorations can be purchased in some of the exclusive stores, they are considered expensive.

Decorating Christmas trees was not widely practised on the island, but is now becoming popular in middle and upper class homes in areas such as Kingston, Montego Bay and Mandeville.

Some families even plant a Christmas tree in their front garden (we were one of those families), and decorate it every year with lights, balloons and home made toys. Others will buy or cut down a small tree (not necessarily evergreen), and decorate it likewise, after setting it up by a living room window, or on the front verandah. Christmas presents are not usually placed under the trees.

The curtains at every window are frilly, pretty and new, whether they are hand made or store bought; and the windows that are glass paned, gleam to match their frilly dresses. All in all, the homes inside and out, are kept as neat and clean as possible throughout the festive season.

A giant evergreen tree, donated by the Government of Canada, traditionally occupies the centre of downtown Kingston, and is beautifully and luxuriously dressed. Various choirs take turn rendering to passersby the old and new versions of carols and hymns. This takes place about a week before, and up to Christmas Eve.

In Kingston's 'downtown,' the traditional Christmas stalls (small, brightly painted portable shops, made specifically for this time of year), are in place and in business. They are closely wedged beside each other in neat rows around the outer perimeter of Queen Victoria Park, or 'Parade,' as it is locally called. The stalls display and sell a variety of Xmas toys, clothing, trinkets and decorations, ninety per cent of which are made by the stall owners and their families.

Throughout Christmas week, people will browse and buy from the stalls, but the high point of shopping is done at 'Christmas Market.' This is a time, rather than a place, and begins at dawn on Christmas Eve, to dawn on Christmas Day.

On Christmas Eve, everyone is dressed in his new finery. Those with relatives abroad would have already received their parcels earlier in the month. Others would have done their shopping for dress and suit materials as early as September, and had their dressmakers and tailors fashion the best styles for them. Everyone has a new footwear, even if it happens to be sneakers (running shoes).

All who are able bring their children, grandchildren, or themselves to Christmas Market. For this occasion, city buses and mini vans are the sane and sensible mode of transportation, as there is no room in Parade for other vehicles. The streets are taken over by pedestrians. Public transportation runs all night, and are always invariably packed to capacity, as the living stream of Christmas Marketers pour into Parade.

Most people will shop all night and then attend church services, which begin as early as five o'clock on Christmas morning. All the churches representing the different denominations – Roman Catholic, Methodist, Anglican, Baptist, Episcopalian, Pentecostal and Presbyterian, have special Christmas Eve and Christmas morning services. These are always well attended.

At this time of year, friendliness flows freely. Everyone goes out of his way to be helpful, kind, and generous to each other, in whatever way they can.

There is an island wide 'open house' on Christmas day. Strangers, as well as relatives and friends, can drop in unannounced, and partake of whatever the host has to offer – a glass of wine, some rum punch, a piece of cake, or sit down with the family to breakfast or dinner.

Carollers from schools, churches, and other organizations, entertain in hospitals, seniors' homes, community centres and/or street corners, right up to Christmas morning. Of course the John Canoe Street Dancers in their diverse costumes and masks, take to the streets to entertain passersby, residents and shoppers alike. These street dances in carnival form, take place from early December until after Christmas, in many towns and villages throughout Jamaica.

And of course there is Santa Clause. Yes, even in Jamaica there is a Santa Clause. In years gone by, Santa was the traditional caucasian fat man (naturally so, or made up to look that way), in his red suit and sporting a long white beard.

In recent times however, Santa Claus arrives in Jamaica the week before Christmas, still on the chubby side, and wearing his traditional suit and beard. But his skin tone ranges from ebony to sandalwood.

Jamaican children are no longer surprised to see a jolly black man (or brown, or yellow) with a white beard, in a red suit, walking across their front yard with a sack on his back, saying "ho! ho! ho!" on the night of Christmas Eve.

Christmas meals no matter how simple, are feasts to the providers. The average breakfast consists of bacon, ham and eggs; or ackee and codfish – a unique and delicious gourmet breakfast which is sometimes served as a supper dish. Harddough bread, roasted breadfruit and/or boiled green bananas. Tea or Blue Mountain coffee flavoured with sweetened condensed milk for the adults, and cocoa or chocolate 'tea' for the children. All have a glass of freshly squeezed orange juice, half of a grapefruit, or a ripe banana, half an hour before breakfast begins.

Everybody snacks on cake, fruits, nuts, or fruit juices until dinner, as there is no set lunch on Christmas day. Families usually sit down to dinner about mid-afternoon.

On a whole, dinner consists of roast chicken (usually home reared), roast or jerk pork or ham, or curried goat. A few homes may serve turkey or duck. Tomato slices on beds of lettuce leaves with sliced cucumbers. Rice and Peas, boiled yellow or white yams, sweet potatoes, and boiled or baked ripe plantains.

The beverage is the traditional Sorrel – a refreshing drink made from the red petals of the Sorrel plant. This drink is brewed, and flavoured with ginger and sweetened to taste. It can be served as a non- alcoholic drink, or with wine and/or rum added for extra flavouring. It is served chilled, or with ice cubes. Carrot juice can also be served.

Another traditional Christmas drink, though not necessarily served at dinner, is the famous Jamaican rum punch. Its flavour and ingredient differ according to the recipes handed down in the various families. Rum punch is served at all Jamaica's festive occasions, and as a welcoming drink to visitors landing at either of the two international airports. My family's rum punch recipe is still a guarded secret.

Dessert is a choice of Christmas cake, plum pudding (rich, dark, moist and loaded with fruits which had been soaking in wine and rum since August, until the early Christmas week baking); or home made ice cream (coconut, soursop, grapenut, pineapple or rum and raisin flavours). In most homes, all of the above desserts are served.

* * * * *

Christmas gifts are usually handed out on Christmas morning after breakfast. Although most of the children would have already bought their toys at Christmas Market. There is almost always a surprise gift for each family member, however small or humble, which is given out at this time.

Gift exchanges between adults are sometimes expensive but far from being extravagant. Some adults would have saved all year (in the bank, or on lay-a-way), in order to get that sequined gown his wife has been longing for; the dinner jacket or suit her husband needed; the velour dressing gown for Grandma; or the beautiful diamond ring, which will give a fellow the courage to ask his girlfriend to marry him. Simple and inexpensive gifts are also given, and gratefully received and cherished.

In Jamaica, this is the time of year when employers show their employees how much they appreciate their loyalty and hard work during the year that's past. Bonuses (pay raises) are given sometimes during Christmas week. Promotions are made, although this is not the only time of year that this is done. Some employers give out food hampers to the families, and/or have dinner parties for employees and their spouses.

The staff on duty in the hospitals are given free meals on Christmas day, and dinner is served by the hospitals' chief of staff including the Matrons (Directors of Nursing). Santa Claus visits the patients as well, and young and old are given gifts.

In the evening and night, entertainment is in the form of 'garden parties' (something akin to North American amusement parks, complete with clowns, merry-go-round and ferris wheels), for children and young at heart adults.

Some people prefer to see a double feature movie at the local cinema, go to one of the many house parties in progress, or drop in on relatives and friends and laugh the night away. Some just stay at home receiving and entertaining friends, and talking about the good old days. This is another night when no one wants to sleep, not even the children, and they are not forced to.

* * * * *

Christmas day in Jamaica, in my recollection, has always been warm and sunny. There is no memory of any rainfall on this day on my island paradise.

December thirty-first – New Years Eve, is important in the island's festivities. Dances and parties go full swing into the wee hours of the morning. Most Jamaicans though, usher in the New Year by attending 'Watch Night Services' from eleven in the evening to midnight, in the various churches.

On the stroke of midnight, all the church bells ring. Ships in the harbour join in by sounding their foghorns, and all over the cities and towns there are firework displays. People hug and kiss each other where ever they are, and wish each other a Happy New Year.

The excitement and frivolities slowly peters off, and by January second, everything has returned to normal.

Christmas in Jamaica is an experience lucky visitors will not readily forget. It leaves you with a joyous, mystical and somewhat romantic feeling. A feeling which haunts you pleasantly, and wills you to go back – at Christmas time.

Christmas in Jamaica for me and other native born, is always boonoonoonos (exceptionally beautiful). So if you want to have a boonoonoonos Christmas, go to Jamaica – No Problem.

Remembering The Candy Shoppe

It was Christmas evening 1991. I had just awakened from an awful dream to discover that I was alone. The eerie silence of the two–storey brick house crept into the bedroom, and my consciousness. The lingering sensation of an obscure dream vanished quickly, as I emerged into wakefulness and realised that I was veiled in the curtains of night.

"Where is everybody?" I screamed in silent panic. Was no one home? I turned over on my left side, and the pain in my back crescendoed, sending rhythmic ripples out to every fibre of my being. I grabbed the wooden bed frame above my head, to stop my fall over the edge, down to the 'mattressed plateau.' And I remembered.

It had been four weeks since my back surgery, and the pain was no less now, than it was on my first post operative day. My activity was limited as I could not walk properly, neither was I able to sit or bend. My husband had reconstructed our double bed into a two–tiered sleeping affair. Using the mattresses from two foldaway cots, he had elevated my sleeping area to a height, easily accessible, and I was able to get in and out without much trouble. A slightly deformed replica of my hospital bed. I referred to his half as the 'mattressed plateau' onto which I almost fell, just now.

The clock radio on my night table told me it was 5.47 pm. It was hardly night, but dark enough. The rest of the family had gone to have Christmas dinner with my husband's cousins in Binbrook. It had been decided earlier that he would bring back his dinner and mine, so that we could eat together.

I thought about going for my prescribed walk, (eighty times through the Kitchen, down the hall, and through the living room, equalling a mile), but since I had difficulty going up and down the stairs, had agreed not to take my walks when alone. I rolled painfully onto my stomach, slid my legs over the side of the bed, and pushed myself into standing position. With back brace in place, I slowly made my way towards the ensuite, and its elevated toilet.

I switched the television on as I passed it, and tossed the converter onto the bed. A children's choir was singing a medley of Christmas carols, ending with 'Joy to the World.' Then the voice of Johnny Mathis took over. "Chestnuts roasting on an open fire..." he sang. And the orange–red flames, like a million armed monster, spread out and up, engulfing the Candy Shoppe with lecherous greed.

* * * * *

I had passed it, and been in many times on my way to and from school. Times when I had forced myself to take the longer route, just so I could smell the confectioneries being made in the small 'factory' adjoining the rear of the shop. Or to feast my eyes on the red and white coconut squares, the trays of peanut brittle and clusters with thre'pence sized peanuts sticking out. And ginger sugar – dark brown, and teeming with sugar cane goodness. They all beautifully graced the glass shelves of the Candy Shoppe, mouth wateringly enticing.

I was about nine years old when I was first introduced to it. "There's a neat sweetie shop just opened on Tower Street, Lynette," my best friend Sonia had announced, as we met at the gate of number 10 Charlotte, where she lived. Her house was a green and white four bedroom bungalow, with shingles on its roof. The large front verandah where we often played with our dolls, overlooked the iron wrought fence and gate, and Charlotte Street.

She had waited there every morning for me, and we would take the short cut around the sides of Barnes Gully, often walking precariously on the concrete edge. Except of course when it rained heavily, and the gully was full of the raging muddy waters of the Hope River, heading down to the sea. We would cross the wooden bridge to Barry Street. Then turned right on Fleet Street to Laws, where our school was situated.

"Lets walk pass there and see it," she had urged, and started west along Tower Street.

"I don't want to be late for school," I said, doing a short jog to catch up with her. We had been late on two previous occasions. Once when we had stopped to inspect Bingo's newborn puppies, we had just barely made it into the classroom before the doors were closed for assembly. The second time we had not been so lucky. We were crossing the bridge towards Barry Street and had seen a small crowd of people gathered, and of course had gone to investigate. It had been Founder, a Rasta man, who had 'captured' an abandoned tin shack at the edge of the gully near Barry about a year before. It was rumoured that he grew and sold ganja plants.

Founder was lying face down on the concrete edge of the gully that morning. He had been stark naked. The heat from the morning sun and the concrete did not seem to bother him, as he did not move.

My keen eyes noticed also that he was not perspiring as it was a logical thing to do. And the most disgusting part of all was the sight of what seemed to me at the time to be hundreds of centipedes crawling out of his long matted red-tinged hair, and running down the side of the gully, and some into the bushes. A young pregnant woman had leaned over the side and vomited, while being supported by another.

We had left just as he was being rolled onto a stretcher. Someone in the crowd had murmured that he was dead.

We were fifty minutes late, and had to remain after school that day to write fifty times in our notebooks <u>I must not be late for school.</u> We hadn't been late since then, and we weren't going to be if I could help it.

"Can't we walk pass it on our way home?" I had asked pleadingly. "It will still be there, won't it ?"

"Of course it will," she had retorted, "but we're almost there now. Its just at the corner of Tower and Fleet Streets. Lets run!" She had grabbed my hand and we started running. My canvas school bag had plopped against my side rhythmically with each stride.

The warm morning breeze gently stroked my face, and I had suddenly become aware of the sweet inviting fragrances of peppermint, toasted coconut, and ginger. I loved ginger – ginger cookies, ginger syrup, and ginger beer. I had heard of ginger sugar, but I had never seen or tasted it.

"I wonder if they make ginger sugar!" It had been more a thought expressed, than a question asked.

"Of course they do." Sonia had answered emphatically. "I should know!" She had added in conspiratorial tones.

Reaching the shop at last, I had gazed in wonder at the delightful sights that greeted my eyes.

It was a small store, shaped like a slice of pie, and glassed on the two long sides, one facing Tower Street, the other Fleet Street. Hanging on each side was a red and white sign written in old English "The Candy Shoppe." The doors to the shop were at its point, like twins.

There were glassed cupboards and cases on the floor and along the walls, as well as on the counter which separated the front of the store from the back. On the left hand corner of the counter sat a cash register, and behind it, in the rounded portion of the pie, stood Sonia's dad, Altimon D'Aguilar.

He was part Chinese, but only his eyes were visible evidence of this. He was tall and medium build, with thick wavy black hair like his daughter's, and a bushy moustache which hid his upper lip. He always had a ready smile for Sonia and I, but not that morning.

"What are you girls doing here?" He had asked with annoyance in his voice. "You are

25

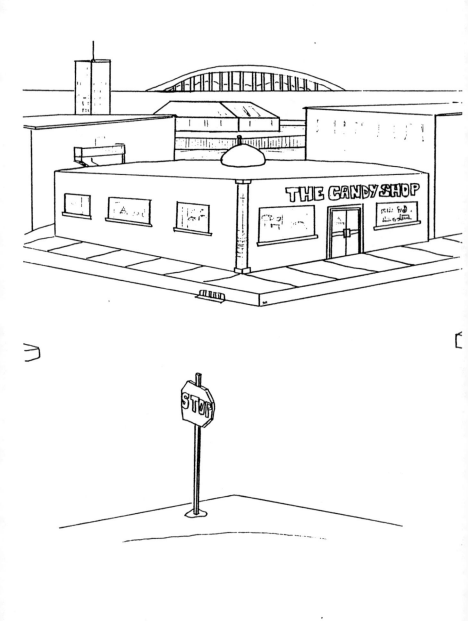

going to be late for school. Do you know what time it is?" His black eyes had looked from Sonia to me, and back to Sonia, apparently awaiting a reply.

"Hi Daddy! I just brought Lynette to show her our new shop; and the ginger sugar are those brown squares over there.."
She had turned to me abruptly and smiled, then back to face her dad. "Right daddy? Lynette has never tasted them. Can we..."

"Come back after school, and I'll save you both a piece. Now run along!" Mr. D'Aguilar had coaxed us, and we did.

We had got to school just in time to join the end of the line, as our class marched into our home room to the tune of 'D'ya ken John Peel,' played on the piano by Miss Newton, our music teacher.

Being a serious minded student, I had settled down to the day's class work, but my thoughts occasionally strayed to the Candy Shoppe, and the treat that was awaiting me at the end of the day.

I will always remember my first piece of ginger sugar. The aromatic smell, and nippy taste of the spice which flavoured the dark moist square made of wet sugar. Mr. D'Aguilar had handed each of us a piece the size of a matchbox, and shooed us home. I had nibbled on mine slowly, savouring every delicious morsel. It was then that ginger sugar became my favourite candy. I never dreamed the day would come when it would bring me grief.

* * * * *

27

Sonia and I were very close. We had known each other since we were six, when mom and I had moved in with Aunt Maude in their old family house at 20 Water Street, shortly after dad had abandoned us. Mom and I had been standing in line in the Victory Bakery, waiting to be served. She was wearing a blue and white polka dot dress with frills around the neck and skirt pockets. We had looked at each other without speaking. Then, "This is my grandma," she had said boastingly. The soft drop curls which clustered her head bounced as she looked at the woman at her side. " She is visiting from St. Catherine. Have you got a grandma?"

"No!" I had said. " They are dead. I've only got Grandpa Salmon, but I've seen him only once. He's English."

"How sad!" Sonia's grandma had responded, looking first at me, then at mom. "Every pretty little girl should have a grandmother. Would you like me to be yours? You wouldn't mind that would you honey?" She had looked down at her granddaughter, ruffling her curls as she spoke. Sonia had let go of her grandma's hand, and took mine. "You could be my sister, couldn't she Grandma? And we can play together." We had moved out onto the pavement and started twirling, laughing as we did, while 'grandma' and mom chatted. It was as if Sonia and I had been friends for ever.

We had shared the same interests, and excelled in the same subjects at school, except English Composition which I was very good at, but which my friend detested. We had spent many hours together – playing, studying, visiting East Street museum and library, investigating 'things,' and combing each other's hair. We each had been accepted as a member of the other's family, and because we looked a bit alike, we often lied to strangers who asked if we were sisters.

We were both small boned with long legs, and loved to run. My friend was lighter complexioned than I was, but we had the same textured hair, which we liked to have combed back, braided or pony-tailed, with fringed bangs on our foreheads. Our dark brown eyes were set in oval shaped faces, and her front teeth were small and even while mine were slightly bucked. We lived about a block from each other, and were always at each others homes.

Sonia and I were eleven years old before her dad had allowed us to help in the shop on Saturdays. Her fifteen year old brother Winston had always worked there part-time since it opened. It was evident he resented our participation, and he had shown intolerance at our blunderings. Before long however, we had became adept at not only serving customers, but making change, wrapping candies, and stocking the shelves.

Sonia's mother Faye had occasionally helped with the baking in the small factory, but her specialty was making peppermint cakes for the shop at Christmas time. They were made of coconut coloured red, green, and candy striped, and this Christmas Eve the shelf was stacked with them.

* * * * *

I had gone to the shop at 4:30 p.m. as was pre-arranged, to help out until closing, so that Sonia and her parents could run their individual

29

last minute errands. I had arrived to find the shop devoid of customers, and Winston was no where to be seen. I had lifted the latch of the half door that connected the shop to the factory, and entered.

"Winston!" I had shouted, looking through into the now deserted factory. "Winston, where are you?" I had heard a muffled sound and a few short bouts of coughing, and Winston had emerged from the small storage closet behind me. His eyes looked moist and pink as he staggered away from the closet towards me.

"What were you doing in there" I had asked, yet not really caring. For although his sister was my best friend, he was not one of my favourite persons. There was something about him that I detested, but could not pinpoint.

"None of your business," he had said between fresh bouts of coughing. There had been a pungent smell of menthol and smoke which followed him out of the closet, and I also detected the same on his breath when he spoke. I had noticed that smell about him before, especially when his parents weren't around.

"I bet you were smoking in there!" I had said. "I can smell cigarette smoke."

"Well its not. And don't go around saying I was smoking, because I wasn't. Understand?" He had poked me in the chest as he walked past me into the shop to serve a newly arrived customer.

We had been so busy with last minute shoppers, that by the time we closed, we had forgotten our earlier argument, and had wished each other a cordial. 'Merry Christmas.'

I had gone home, had supper, and started getting ready for Christmas Market. Sonia and I had got permission to go by ourselves for the first time. It was 7 p.m., and she was shouting for me at the gate. She had saved for me a special box of ginger sugar, and had left it at the Candy Shoppe. She would go on ahead and retrieve it. I would meet her there as soon as I was ready, then we would go on to Christmas Market from there.

"I still think you girls should have an adult with you." My mother had said, as she tied the plaid ribbon at the end of my ponytail. The ribbon matched my taffeta dress with the frills at the hem and neck. Sonia had been wearing her pink voile, the same style as mine. My mom had made both our dresses for my last birthday party.

"Its going to be very crowded down town tonight you know?" She continued. "Why don't I..."

"We'll be alright Mom," I had said in pleading tones. I had looked forward to being grown-up and responsible, and I didn't want Mom, who was a worrywart, to change her mind. "I promise we'll be fine Mom." I continued. "We'll meet you and Aunt Maude at Sasso's at eleven."

"I still don't like it," she had flung back at me, then – "Get away from there you mongrel!" She had run onto the front porch in her slip, shouting at Man, who had just cocked his leg against her favourite Hibiscus bush.

I had put the five shilling note that mom had given me, with the seventeen shillings and sixpence I had saved from my earnings at the Candy Shoppe, in the zippered compartment of my straw handbag, and slung it over my left shoulder. Aunt Maude had given me the purse the previous Christmas. Dear Aunt Maude. I

loved her as much as I did Mom. She had been a
pillar of strength for us after Dad's desertion.

She was very much like Mom physically.
Both were petite with round faces and big brown
eyes. Unlike Mom's, Aunt Maude's nose was
prominent and her teeth were even and white.
She often wore her curly black hair in a pageboy
style, while Mom wore hers loosely around her
head, or up in a bun.

Aunt Maude was a third grade school
teacher at Central Branch Elementary. Mom
worked as a stenographer at Sasso and Sasso, a
small law firm in the heart of downtown Kingston.
Mom's company was having their office party
that Christmas Eve. My aunt was meeting her
there, and Sonia and I was to Join them after we
had finished shopping, "and not later than
eleven." I had felt good that Mom was allowing me
to do this, and vowed I would make her proud of
me.

"See you later Mom." I had said, quickly
kissing her on the cheek. As I closed the gate, I
had heard the sounds of fire engines going west
on Tower Street. My heart had leapt in my chest.
I always felt nervous and uneasy whenever I saw
or heard fire engines. I had an unexplainable
fear of fires, although I had never seen or
experienced one.

By the time I got to Tower and Charlotte
Streets, I had noticed people running towards
Fleet, and there was a traffic policeman re-
directing traffic left on Charlotte to Harbour
Street. I could see billows of smoke ahead, rising
and enveloping the sky in the vicinity of Fleet
and Tower Streets.

Dusk had merged unnoticed into night,
and I could see no stars above. A sense of fear

overcame me, and I started to run as fast as I could, as were others around me. My face was wet, but I was not sure if it was from perspiration or tears. Some inner sense, it seemed, had alerted me to the fact that the Candy Shoppe was on fire, before I even saw it.

The crowd, held at bay by policemen, was almost as dense as the orange tinged smoke which engulfed the Candy Shoppe. The air was hot and heavy, and the strong smell of burning confectionery could be detected in the suffocating smoke. The sound of an ambulance moving away, was heard, at which time the crowd enmasse moved a bit closer to the fire. A voice on bullhorn had shouted for them to move back. Winston's face with his moist pink eyes as he emerged from the closet, then filled my mind.

"They found a child in there close to the door," a female voice in the crowd had offered. "....Badly burned," said another. Sonia! She had gone back to retrieve a box of ginger sugar for me!

"Nooooooo! Sonia! Sonia! Sonia!"

I had pushed through the crowd with a strength I did not know I possessed, and ran across the street towards the inferno. Just then there had been a loud explosion, and the sound of shattering glass. And the orange–red landscape like a mighty flood, had filled the sky, the ground, my head, expanding ever outward from its core, the Candy Shoppe.

* * * * *

Sonia was buried on December 28th, the day before my release from hospital, where I was treated for heat prostration, smoke inhalation,

33

shock and facial lacerations from splintering glass.

No one had spoken directly to me about the fire and Sonia's death, but I did piece bits of conversations I overheard from time to time, and came to the conclusion that her death was a brutal one. She had lost all her hair in the fire – her beautiful, beautiful hair!

I never saw the D'Aguilar family again. My mom had told me that they had moved away to St. Catherine where Mr. D'Aguilar was originally from, and two weeks later when I was well enough to leave the house, I had gone to 10 Charlotte Street and discovered that it was so.

I found a new route to school, so that I did not have to pass by Sonia's house, or the site where the Candy shoppe stood. That part of my life became locked away in a corner of my mind, and was kept submerged until now.

* * * * *

"I'm dreaming of a white Christmas," the bass voice crooned. I switched on the bathroom lights, and stared unbelievingly at my reflection in the mirror. My face was awash with tears. Thirty five years of unshed tears. I had never had the courage to consciously mourn the loss of my friend. If I had done so, I would have had to acknowledge the fact that she was gone forever, perishing in an inferno created by the carelessness of her brother, and because she had gone back to get a box of ginger sugar for me.

I had never said goodbye to Sonia. Never visited her resting place, or cried for her, until now. I felt relieved, refreshed. It was as if a

34

light had flooded the dimmed recesses of my mind. In the darkness of my bathroom, on that Christmas night, I had confronted a past sorrow, wrestled with it, and overcame.

I shuffled painfully out to my desk in the upstairs hallway, took out my notepad and pencil, and wrote as the thoughts flowed freely from my mind:

There'll be peppermint cakes in the Candy
Shoppe,
In just a while, it will be Christmas;
And the wonderful store where we children
stop
Will have goodies for each lad, and each lass.
The sweet smiles that we wear,
The laughter that you hear,
Will echo loud and long,
In the Candy Shoppe song.

As I wrote the last stanza of this tribute to my friend, I heard the front door open.

"Dinner is served!" My husband shouted gleefully up to me. "Dinner for two!"

"I'll set this verse to music," I thought. I think Sonia would have liked that.

Poinsettia and Holly.

The warm Jamaican December afternoon had merged unnoticed into the cold dark Canadian night. After my initial fascination with the take–off, and viewing the dark green shapes of the islands below, I had immersed myself into my thoughts.

Would I like it in Canada? I had heard and read of incidents of racial discrimination and bigotry there.

"How do I know I'll get along with white Canadians?" I had asked Mirriam, my anxiety getting the better of me.

"You'll just be yourself," she had answered. "The rest will fall into place."

"How strange," I thought when I disembarked and waited to go through the various official channels before being allowed into Canada as a Landed Immigrant. Only a few hours ago I was in warm Jamaica, home at Poinsettia Path.

And now I was in a new country on Christmas Eve, about to embark on a new adventure, a brand new way of life. I looked unseeingly at the human traffic as it passed by me while I waited, and I could see, smell, hear and touch the things in and around the house at home.

The house in Manchionele sat on a hill

overlooking the steep, winding parochial road which leads to Butcher's Park. The long, unpaved gravel driveway connected the road with the terrazzo–tiled verandah and steps, and was flanked on either side by beautiful poinsettia bushes growing in even rows. Their red blooms added splendour to the golden crowned tropic morning.

This was December and the poinsettias were in full bloom. I had looked down on those bushes from my vantage point on the verandah, many times before, but this morning it was somehow different. I was leaving Poinsettia Path today, maybe for the last time.

A Doctor bird had flown across my path and perched on the number eleven mango tree which grew amidst the poinsettia bushes on the right, close to the entrance–way. It was a healthy tree, but had not grown much taller than the bushes, unlike others of its kind.

Mirriam had once said jokingly, that it was presumptuous enough to grow in and amongst the poinsettias, but that at least it had the decency to retard its growth so as not to overshadow its neighbours or look too out of place.

Mirriam always talked like that. I remembered her having frequent weird one-sided conversations with the plants and trees on our property; scolding them if they looked a bit droopy, and praising them when they appeared healthy and lush.

"They can hear and feel just like humans you know?" She had said to me once when I inquired as to why she was talking to the plants.

With one arm slung casually around my neck, she had explained how the trees and plants

38

picked up human vibrations, and responded to their pain, fear, joy and mirth.

"For instance, see that mango tree there?" She had pointed with her eyes to the dwarfed number eleven, then continued while stroking the gaping petals of a white hibiscus flower.
"When Mom and Dad died in that horrible accident, it knew, and it cried".

"Cried?" I had asked, taken aback by what she was saying.

"Yes," she had replied calmly. "Even before we got the news, that mango tree knew. I sensed something was wrong when all its leaves started to droop, and it began dropping its young fruits."

I had then turned towards her and noticed that her face had a sad and wistful look as it always did whenever she was remembering. She had looked away across the deserted country road towards some distant place none other could perceive.

"When the policeman came that afternoon to tell us of the train crash," she had continued, "there was not a single fruit left on that tree. It didn't bear again for two years."

"Was it mourning like we were?" I had asked in my childish innocence. Like my sister, I loved the outdoors, and was always interested in her philosophies regarding plants. I wanted to drink in every word she uttered so wisely and with such eloquence.

"Oh yes, it was," she had responded emphatically. "That was Mom's favourite tree on the property you know? She said it grew from a seed dropped there in cow dung, when the surrounding area was pasture land. That was before Dad had put up the fence. Mom used to sit under it some evenings and read. Sometimes she would read to us."

My sister had walked away from the hibiscus and had begun 'petting' the leaves of the June Rose, her favourite bush.

"I think the tree has healed now, more or less. Just as we are doing. See how it is bearing?"

I had looked passed her head and stared at the mango tree, seeing in its shade a diminutive olive skinned woman, holding her daughters on her knees and reading to them the story of Christopher Robin and Winnie The Pooh!

* * * * *

This morning I had awakened early, not having slept well. I guess I had suffered from anxiety, nervousness or both. After saying goodbye to Aunt Esther as she left for her day at the market, I had walked along the footpath which led from the back of our property to the river. I had jumped across the ribbon-wide sluggish water, and clambered nimbly up the side of Vesper Hill to the Anglican church and the small cemetery at its rear.

I had taken this path a thousand times it seems since my parents' death. For the first few years until I was about eight, I had gone with Mirriam by the 'short cut,' or with an adult who usually used the main road. Then when I was older and more confident, I started going on my own.

Mirriam always took June Rose, red, and white and pink, and I would take 'Ramgoat Roses'. "Periwinkle is the proper name," my sister always reminded me each time I used the

40

local name. Its delicate looking pink, mauve, and white flowers made me think of Titania of fairy stories, rather than the medicinal properties the plant was supposed to be famous for.

I had been going to the cemetery alone since my sister left the country, arranging the flowers as per usual in jam jars, on either side of each headstone. This morning's visit took on a sombre tone. I had not been able to say goodbye to my parents when they died, now I was here to say it to their spirits, and it was very hard. I had lingered longer than I had ever done before, looking at the dark marble headstones bearing their names and date of birth and death; and seeing, as if on a movie screen, a couple in their mid thirties boarding a Jamaica Government Railway passenger train in Kingston, on that fateful August morning seventeen years ago, heading for home and their two young daughters, but never ever reaching them.

* * * * *

Both Mom and Dad had been school teachers. Dad taught general Biology and Mathematics at Dinthill Secondary School, and Mom English and Geography at Westover Preparatory in Manchionele.

They had met at Teachers' College and got married immediately after graduation. Seven months later Mirriam had been born, establishing the fact that Mom did have a 'bun in the oven' when she had got married.

Audrey and David Bentley had waited seven years to have me, while they completed post graduate studies. They had wanted the freedom and ease to look after Mirriam

41

themselves without undue stress which might affect their studies. But when I did arrive they were happy and content with their little family.

Mom and Dad were returning home from Kingston where they had attended a four day Teachers' Conference at Shortwood College. It was the beginning of the Independence holiday weekend, and because of the large number of people travelling that day, extra coaches were added to the train for better service.

As was explained to me in later years when I could better understand, the driver of the forward engine braked suddenly to avoid a large bolder on the tracks, probably caused by landslides from rains the previous night. It was rumoured that the engineer was drunk and unable to respond in time.

The coaches buckled and plunged down the side of a deep gorge, a few miles out of Kendall Station. Mangled bodies, pieces of metal, and luggage were strewn over a great distance from the site of the derailment. Fifty-seven passengers survived. They had all occupied the last two coaches which had remained on the tracks.

Mom had died on impact, with head and internal injuries, a severed right leg (which was never found), broken arms and a severed left breast.

Dad had died on the way to hospital. He had suffered severe head injuries, multiple fractures, and ruptured liver and spleen.

Three days later after the gruesome task of identifying the bodies, my uncle and maternal grandmother had brought them home for burial.

The caskets were closed, but there had been photographs of them on display. The picture of Mom in a high necked black dress, showed her smiling silently, showing off even white teeth and bright, oval inquiring eyes. Black ringlets fringed her forehead and hung below her ears. She was beautiful.

Dad's showed him standing almost at attention, dressed in a light coloured suit. He was unsmiling. His black curly hair was parted in the centre and he wore a thin moustache. Mirriam looks a lot like him. I had never seen those photos before, nor have I since.

My dad's only relatives, two older brothers, had come home from England where they lived, to attend the funeral. They returned two weeks later. My only grandparent, my Mom's mother, had collapsed at the funeral and died a month later of a heart attack. Thus our sorrow was compounded.

Although I cannot remember in detail everything that took place then, I recall the throngs of people inside and outside the church, and the funeral service that seemed to have gone on forever. I recall Uncle Willie lifting me up so that I could place the bunch of Periwinkle on my parents' caskets, and my sister crying and crying and could not be comforted. I also remember the overpowering sickly sweet smell of Kananga Water, not only at the funeral, but at Poinsettia Path after the 'wake'. I have never been able to use perfume, or appreciate its fragrance since.

* * * * *

Aunt Esther, my mother's maiden aunt had come to live with us – to take care of us and the home. Her presence in the household was needed and necessary, but although she was loving, kind and very patient, she was never able to soothe and comfort me, or offer the warmth and understanding that my sister could.

Mirriam was eleven when our parents died, and she took over where Mom left off. Aunt Esther cooked and cleaned and shopped, but it was Mirriam who attended to my personal needs, and promised she'd look after me forever. When I approached the threshold of womanhood, it was my sister who taught me the use of sanitary napkins, and cautioned me about how I should behave around boys.

She did most things for and with me as we grew, and always seemed to know when I needed to be hugged. We grew closer each day.

Aunt Esther never seemed to mind, but some years later I overheard her talking to Mirriam, saying that she had been robbed of her childhood and forced to grow up too soon, "because you took over being mother to Joy, when you should have been enjoying your own childhood."

I was twelve then, and had just come in from school without anyone knowing I had arrived. My aunt was peeling green bananas and dropping them in the Dutch pot on the stove, talking as she worked, without looking at my sister who was sitting at the kitchen table.

Mirriam had stood up and faced Aunt Esther, and in a stern voice said, "I love my sister and always will. We're all that's left of our family, and I'll continue to be there for her for as long as she needs me. My parents would have wanted it that way."

She had turned to walk away, when Aunt Esther took her hands and apologised saying that she meant no harm. Then my sister had softened and hugging her said,"Of course you didn't. I guess I am upset because I have to go away to Kingston and leave her behind."

I had gone back outside and sat under Mom's mango tree, my heart feeling tight within my chest. My throat was dry and itchy and tears had filled my eyes. I had known that my sister was going away to the University of the West Indies in Kingston to study, but hearing her say it just then made it sound so final. I had felt like I was losing my mother all over again.

Sitting there alone with my thoughts, it had suddenly occurred to me that Mirriam did have her own life to live, and a future to prepare for. She had relinquished her childhood for me as my Aunt had said, because she loved and cared about me. She would not do well if she thought that I was unhappy at her leaving. I mustn't let her see me crying, or think that I did not want her to go. After all, I loved her too and wanted what was best for her. If she succeeded, so would I. She was my best friend, my role model, all I had.

* * * * *

My Grand Aunt had always been kind and dependable, and had agreed to stay on at Poinsettia Path to look after things with the help of Daisy our weekly help, and Uncle Willie who agreed to drop in from time to time to make sure all was going well.

I had asked her to accompany me to the airport, but she was unable or unwilling to break her habit of going to the market on a Friday. (I was sure this weekly ritual was more to fraternize with her old cronies and gossip, than to obtain supplies). So she had gracefully declined the offer.

A lone John Crow had flown by, a Pichiarie hot on his tail. "God!" I had thought, "those little birds do drive the crows crazy!" Their fleeting presence had disturbed the Doctor bird, causing him to abandon the limb on which he was perched. He had circled, then headed back to the Mango tree. His iridescent plumage glistened in the morning sunlight.

The pampas green Vauxhall Viva turned off the road and onto the driveway. Uncle Willie had switched off the ignition, opened his door and hopped out of the car, all in one motion it seemed. He had always done that for as long as I had known him. It drove his wife Lillian, crazy whenever she rode with him. "You're going to have an accident one of these days, doing that," she would say."I hope to God I'm not in the car with you when it happens." And he would just dismiss her with a boyish grin.

" Well Joy, ready for your trip?"

My mother's younger brother had stood in the front yard with his right foot resting on the bottom step of the verandah. He had come as planned, to drive me to Norman Manley Airport. The back of his pink Bushjacket–styled shirt was already damp with perspiration, although it was only nine o'clock, and the December morning was cooler with the wafting of the Christmas breeze.

"You saying farewell to the place?" He'd flashed his familiar wide smile, then leaped onto the verandah, picking up two of the cases and taking them down to the car. I had smiled back sheepishly. Uncle Willie, like my sister, always seemed able to read my mind.

46

"I guess I was, as a matter of fact," I had replied. "I have been taking in the beauty of the place, willing my mind to memorize it all." I had picked up my handbag and overnight case from the wooden chaise lounge. "I'm sure going to miss home," I said and meant it. "Do you want a drink before we go?" Although my uncle liked a drink or two of Appleton Estate Special, he never drank anything strong before noon, so my offer of a drink, for both of us, meant an ice-cold fruit juice or Ting, which he liked.

"Hell no," he had replied, putting the third case in the trunk and slamming it shut. "We'd better hit the road before it gets too busy. Your flight leaves at what, two o'clock?" I had nodded. "It will give you time to catch your breath, then lose it again by chatting with Lil, before you board."

"I thought Aunt Lil wasn't coming," I chipped in. "Did she change her mind?"

"Oh, she's joining us at the airport."

"Fine," I had said, "lets go!"

As if to say goodbye, the Doctor bird had emerged from the thick foliage of the number eleven. His long greenish blue tail feathers waving in the breeze. He had perched on one of the poinsettia bushes and began his trill.

I had sat beside my uncle and gazed out the window as we slowly backed off our poinsettia lined driveway onto the road and away from Poinsettia Path, my home.

* * * * *

"Whe' yu goin' bredda-man?" Rufus Green, an employee at the cricket club nearby, and a family acquaintance, had come running

47

after the Viva, as it screeched to a stop. "Yu goin' pass Duncans bredda?'

"Yes, we going to MoBay, hop in."

Rufus was in the back seat before the last two words were uttered, and had promptly engaged my uncle in lively discussions. They had moved from politics to sports to trade, and tried to involve me at intervals in the conversation.

"....so yu going to Canada to join Miss Mirriam, Miss Joy? A t'ink that's a very wise decision yu made, Miss." It always amazed me at the skill Rufus had, mixing Patois and grammatical English, in a way that made sense and even sounded intelligent.

"I think the decision was more or less made for her," Uncle Willie had piped in before I had a chance to come out of my reverie and respond. "Her sister insisted that they should be together, or at least be close by each other. Right Joy?"

"Right," I had answered, wanting to be left alone with my thoughts.

"I need a change anyway," I had heard myself saying. "I understand that nursing in Canada is about the same as it is here, and the salary is two hundred per cent better." Rufus whistled in surprise. "I'll see how I like it."

"Poinsettia Path aint goin' to be de same widdout you, Miss Joy. No sah! But is good dat Esther is living there. She is family, so she wi' tek care a' it fi yu."

I had leaned back against the seat of the Viva and closed my eyes, trying to occlude the conversation going on between the two men. I was starting to get that homesick feeling as I did when I had gone away to Nursing School at Mona,

48

only this time it felt worse.

* * * * *

Mirriam had graduated from the University of the West Indies with a B.A. in Biology, and had applied, and was accepted to the University of Guelph in Ontario, Canada, to pursue her Master's degree. I was almost eighteen, and six months into my nursing course when she left for Canada. I had obtained a two-day pass out of Residence, so that I could spend time with her before she left.

She had taken me to dinner at Jules' in Constant Spring. I had ordered curried shrimps and my sister, 'Jerk Chicken'. I remembered not being able to finish the meal because it was too peppery. I could never tolerate hot pepper as well as Mirriam did. After the meal, we had gone to see 'The Defiant Ones' at The Carib, and shortly after the movie was in progress I had realized that my 'period' had started after experiencing sudden lower abdominal cramps. On retreating seconds later to the washroom to investigate, I had discovered that not only was it early, but it had ruined the back of my new peau de soir skirt.

To avoid embarrassment, we had left the dimly lit cinema while the movie was in progress, and laughed about it later at Mirriam's apartment, when she insisted on re-enacting how we slinked out of the cinema like thieves, with her walking close behind me to help me hide my bloodied rear.

The rest of the time we had spent just chatting about anything and everything. We talked about boys, about love and sex. It was

49

then that she revealed to me that she was no longer a virgin. She had lost it to a fellow named Alphonse from Cayman Brac, with whom she had gone steady in her second year at university. He had been called away home because of a family crisis, and never returned to classes, never wrote to her, nor replied to any of the letters she had written him.

"At first I was devastated over it. The fact that I had been intimate with him, and now he was out of my life was very hard to take. I thought then that I loved him, but now I think that I had used him as a source of strength at a time when mine might have been weak and I needed someone to uphold me." She had giggled girlishly as she tossed her underwear in the suitcase she was packing. "I got over him though, after talking it through with a few of my psychology major friends. I didn't even have to pay. Joy, what's the matter?" She had interrupted her packing to stare at me with concern. Then I realized that I had been frowning, and feeling angry inside.

"You never mentioned this to me before," I had said in the curt cold voice I could not believe was mine. I had never spoken a harsh word to her before, nor had I ever felt this angry. "I didn't even know you had a boyfriend, let alone having had sex with him. I tell you all my secrets, even when that Webster boy chased me down the gully and touched my breasts. Even when...."

"I couldn't talk to you about such things then, silly." She had hugged me and stroked my hair as she often had done when I was younger and needed to be comforted.

"Why not?" I had demanded, softening a little.

"Because then, you were like my daughter. You were too young to be burdened with such things. But I'm telling you about it now, aren't I?" Tipping my chin, she had looked me straight in the eyes, and I nodded.

"Do you know why I've told you?" But before I could answer, she continued."I've told you now because you're older and able to understand and not be judgemental. You are not only my younger sister, but my compatriot, a fellow professional, though you have a couple of years to go to make it legally so." She smiled teasingly and stood back a bit from me, still holding my gaze.

"I have told you this most intimate thing because you are my best friend, and will always be."

We had hugged each other for the longest time, and I had felt ashamed. Ashamed of my selfishness and inadequacy in not being able to be of help to my sister when she needed it, as she always had been to me. But out of the turmoil of my thoughts, I had realized with instant clarity that because of our age difference, my sister would always be matriarchal to me. My best attempt at reciprocating was to be her best friend. After all she was mine too. I told her so.

Minutes after the plane took off, I had stood there rooted to the spot. My face was awash with tears and an overwhelming sense of loneliness had gripped my heart. My sister, my mother, my friend was gone away from me and I may never see her again!

"As soon as you've finished your nursing course, you must go to her." Uncle Willie had taken my hand and awkwardly tried his best to comfort me. "You two belong together and nothing should keep you apart." He had promised to be there for me whenever I needed him.

"I'm only a phone call away, right?"

"Right!" I had echoed, drying my eyes with the back of my hand.

My uncle had kept his word. He always seemed to sense when I was in need of a diversion or reassurance, and often called me from his home or office in MoBay. At times he would drive to Mona to visit me and take me on the town.

When he married Lillian Dunne, a Registered Nurse from Falmouth, she became my aunt in every sense of the word. She was five years older than my uncle, but they loved and respected each other.

She often gave me nursing tips, and sometimes coached me for exams. She had tried her best to fill the void Mirriam's absence had left in my life, and in a way she did. But it was not the same.

I had missed being with my sister, telling her things. Things much too intimate to talk about on the phone or explain in letters. I missed hearing her talk and sing to the plants. Seeing her beautiful face reflecting strength and determination. And having that peace of mind that I did belong to a loving family. For although I was strongly independent and had been so even as a small child, there was the need to hold onto my family and keep the bond unbroken.

I hardly went out on dates, and was never really serious with any one boy. Instead I had immersed myself in my studies, determined to do well and graduate on time. I always kept in mind a phrase Mirriam once quoted to me about knowing where you have been in order to know where you were going.

In my final year of nursing school, proceedings for my immigration to Canada were initiated by my sister. She had now received her Master's Degree in Biology and was teaching at a Community College in Brantford where she lived. I was very excited about the prospect and began my own preparations.

Two days before my graduation, Mirriam had surprised me by coming home for the ceremony. At the airport with my aunt and uncle, I was of the opinion that we were there to meet a friend of theirs, and as we milled around in the arrival lounge waiting, my mind was occupied with my pending position at the University Hospital which I was to start in a month. I was thinking of the need to gain as much experience in the nursing field as possible, so that I would be able to cope well in Canada. And then I had seen her.

She was impeccably groomed, and her outfit emphasized her height and slim built. She wore her wavy black hair in a ponytail with a few wispy strands fringing her smooth olive forehead. She looked more beautiful than I had known her to be, and as our eyes met, they mirrored the joy of the moment. For a brief while we had just stood and stared at each other, and then I ran into the arms of my darling, darling sister.

She had only got a week off, but was able to finalize arrangements for my trip to Canada before she returned. That was seven long, busy months ago. And as I rode to the airport this

53

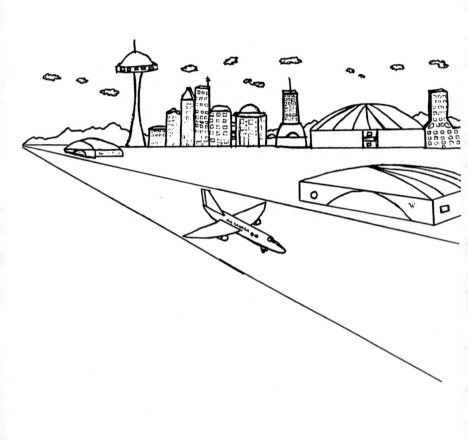

morning, I knew that I was leaving behind all that I knew and was accustomed to. All that was mine. Reading the Sunday Gleaner and the comic strip by Leandro. Picking breadfruit, ackees and mangoes from the trees on our own property. Using my teeth to strip a piece of sugar cane, and enjoying its juicy goodness. Walking barefooted down to the Razor River and skinny dipping if it pleased me. And visiting my parents in their still cold abode in the churchyard atop Vesper Hill.

What would nursing be like in Canada? Would the patients be just as demanding, unreasonable, vulnerable, sick as those I have nursed here at home? Would I like being there? I must confess that I was feeling rather anxious and afraid.

"I'll miss my home and all it represents. I'll miss Poinsettia Path, and Mom's number eleven mango tree."

"Of course you will, hon," my uncle's voice had broken into my reverie, and I realized that I was thinking aloud.

"Nobody said you wouldn't. Esther will be looking after the property, and I will lend a hand as often as I can." He had stretched across and patted my hand. "You'll adjust readily to living in Canada. Mirriam did."

"I know," I responded. "I was just thinking out loud." I had turned around to acknowledge Rufus and discovered that he was gone and we were nearing the airport.

"When did Rufus get out?" I had asked, surprised at his absence.

"Oh, I dropped him off at Duncans Square twenty minutes ago. We thought you were asleep."

"I guess I must have dosed off," I had lied. "I never heard him leave." I had looked out at the montage of scenes flying pass, and pictured the tearful good-byes I would be enduring very shortly. I began to wish that I had arranged my departure for sometime after Christmas. But then I thought "Christmas is a time for families, and Mirriam is mine."

* * * * *

Five hours after leaving Jamaica, I was re-united with my sister, and met for the first time, my brother- in-law to be.

"Welcome to Canada, Joy, I'm Robert Muir. No doubt you know of me. I've heard a lot about you."

He was tall, medium built with fair complexion, and could pass for white, but I knew he wasn't. His mother Margaret was caucasian, and his dad hailed from Grenada. He was a high school teacher of Math and Physical Education. They had met a year before at a seminar, and became engaged seven months later. The wedding was planned for the following June.

Robert's warm hug and smiling face were very reassuring. "It's very nice to meet you at last, Robert," I said looking past him to my sister. I saw the unmistakeable sign of love and happiness in her eyes, and I was pleased. All her life had been devoted to looking out for my welfare. Now she had found someone who would look out for hers.

"And I am his younger brother Brandon." The owner of the voice had come up from behind, and startled me a little. I turned around and looked into the grey eyes of the most handsome man I had ever met. He was as tall as his brother with the same winning smile, but darker, and with wavy brown hair. He was about my age, or a bit older.

At that moment something happened to my heart. I'm not quite sure what it was, but the effects left me somewhat unnerved. As if an electric shock had been sent through my body.

When I regained my composure, I extended my hand and said "Hi!" He took both and kissed me lightly on the lips, and more sparks ignited.

"I have to run," he said, hugging my sister briefly and touching his brother on the shoulder. "You're having dinner at our parents on Boxing Day, I'm told. I'll see you then Joy. I'm looking forward to it." He winked at me and disappeared through the sliding doors.

During the car ride 'home,' visions of Brandon kept popping into my mind. I had met him for just a moment, but the impact it had on me made it seem as if I had known him forever. I learned that he was an un-attached second year Psychology student at MacMaster University in Hamilton, a steel city set like a jewellery box, about twenty minutes drive from Brantford. I was pleased.

* * * * *

It was the night before Christmas, and I had just finished my first meal in Canada. After Robert had toasted us, Mirriam stood up, wine glass in hand.

"To celebrate Christmas this year, I have decided to decorate with poinsettias and holly." She cleared her throat and glanced at Robert, then fixed her gaze on me. "The poinsettias – to celebrate my little sister's presence here with me, and to remind us of a home in Manchionele called Poinsettia Path which will always be ours. The holly," she shifted her gaze to Robert's and smiled in a girlish manner, "to signify our acceptance of our new home here in Canada, and my acceptance of a wonderful Canadian, as my husband to be. Both these plants," she continued, waxing eloquently as she was wont to do without much prompting if the subject is plants, "have traditional significance at this time of year. And so I raise my glass to the poinsettias." We all looked at the beautiful red-bloomed plant in its tinsel-draped flower pot, gracing the dining table. I began to feel a touch of homesickness, and quickly took a sip from my glass.

"And to the holly," Mirriam concluded. I followed their gazes to a large flower pot on the floor by the living room window. It housed a tall green-leafed plant with branches laden with red berries. (I found out later that it was an artificial plant).

"To the poinsettia and the holly, and to the three of us." We clicked our glasses, and after kissing me lightly, Robert pulled his fiancee into his arms, and they kissed passionately.

I felt privileged to be a part of this happy loving scene. I looked past their embracing forms, through the darkness of the Canadian night, and saw a driveway avenued with red poinsettia bushes, glorifying a warm December day.

The dam which held my tears for as long as I could remember, broke, sending the torrent cascading down my cheeks. And as they flowed unchecked, I knew that these were tears of happiness. The happiness which had eluded me for such a long time.

For the first time since we were left orphans, I realized that my sister needed me as much as I did her. We were all that was left of a fragmented family, clinging tenaciously to the love which held it firmly together.

"You two belong together," Uncle Willie had said four and a half years ago. He was right.

My Most Memorable Christmas

The air was crisp and cold, and there was a stinging edge to the wind which blew, pushing us forward into a brisk walk, along the Old North Road.

My friend June and I, experienced the coldest day since we arrived in this Scottish community three weeks ago. Indeed it was the coldest day of our young lives.

Six months after graduating as registered nurses in our native Jamaica, we had decided without much deliberation, that we would go to Scotland to pursue a Midwifery course. This, we felt, would not only give us the opportunity to add "S.C.M." (State Certified Midwife), to the already well earned " Registered Nurse" to our names, but it would serve to satisfy the wanderlust in us that had suddenly without warning, taken over our being.

There is no definite explanation for the reason we chose Scotland. I can only say that because we had decided to do Midwifery during our travels, and because Scotland was rumoured to be the 'Motherland of Midwifery,' we decided to go there.

Neither of us had travelled out of Jamaica before. We were young (twenty years old), and very naive, and we thought it would be an exciting prospect to look forward to.

We had arrived at Bellshill Maternity Hospital on a cool, sunny, Scottish Tuesday, after travelling thousands of miles from Palisados Airport in Kingston, Jamaica, across the Atlantic to Scotland, after a week stopover in London.

As it was a night flight, we had slept through most of it, primarily because of exhaustion from the many farewell parties and visits we endured during the last week before our departure.

We arrived in Bellshill by train, and were quite impressed with the beauty of the countryside, the friendliness of the people, (though they were difficult to understand at first), and our hospitable surroundings. More so, we were pleased to discover that the climate was tolerable.

The landscape surrounding the hospital was very picturesque, and June and I had taken to going on short jaunts, climbing the coal 'bings' nearby, investigating the many small streams which skirted some of these bings, and getting the feel of the countryside.

We usually took our little trips on our days off.

Today was one of those jaunting days for us. It was Christmas Eve, a day which started out being sunny, though far from being warm. Coming from the Tropics, we naturally equated sunshine with warmth.

When we had left on foot for Bellshill Square two hours before, the sun was shining. The lines of emaciated looking trees which lined both sides of the Old North Road, were feathered with frost, and glistened as the cold rays of the winter sun danced among their branches. My watch said 2:40 p.m. We had finished browsing in Bellshill Square, and headed back to MacDougall

House on the hospital grounds, were we lived. We were shocked. It seemed as if we had fallen asleep and awakened to a new day. This was not the same weather as when we left the hospital only two hours ago! It was cold, and dark and blustering. The icy fingers of the wind howling around us reached right in through our fur lined winter coats and pulled the warmth from our bodies.

Knowing that it would be twenty minutes before we would get a bus back to our abode, we made the unwise decision to walk.

We were half way there and freezing. In my opinion, I was properly dressed for the weather, but it was now obvious that that was not so. We both had on our winter coats which June's aunt had bought for us in the United States a few months before we left home, and which we had brought with us to Scotland. Mine was black, and June's bottle green, and the collars, sleeves, and hemlines were trimmed with matching 'fur'. We had on scooter scarves covering our heads, necks, and chins; 'fur'lined gloves which were doing a poor job of keeping our hands warm, and boots.

BOOTS!

I had developed an aversion to the ugly unfashionable things which my boots certainly were, and to date, had stuck to my secret pledge never to put them on my feet.

FEET! What feet? I did not have any! I could not feel them! Silent panic overtook my frozen being.

" I'm frozen stiff! My feet are numb!" I shouted through the thick smoke gushing out of my mouth in spurts with each word that I spoke, and each breath exhaled. It was as if I was smoking an invisible cigarette.

June was walking nimbly, slightly ahead of me, her feet snug, warm and secure in her much needed winter boots. Her scarfed head and neck were a continuous woollen line, ending at the hem of her coat which hid the top of her knee high, fir-trimmed boots. Her boots, though similar to mine, looked neater and more fashionable on her dainty size four feet, than mine did in my size eight.

She was always a fast walker, but she was putting extra effort into her strides now, as if her life depended on it. She turned slightly towards me, cold induced tears welling up in her eyes.

"How come you didn't wear your boots?" she asked through half frozen lips, too stiff to articulate properly. "My feet are frozen, and I am wearing boots. I can imagine how yours must feel! You can't afford to swap comfort for pride in these...." The wind severed the end of her sentence as she turned and increased her strides.

"I didn't know it would get so cold," I pleaded to her back.

" Lets hurry", June shouted over her shoulder, and immediately obeyed her command. I moved my warm tongue over my cold and numbing lips, then pulled it back quickly before it too froze. I thought of a garden lizard on a branch of a mango tree in my Jamaican back garden, with his tongue darting in and out, and smiled an invisible smile.

I looked down at my black stiletto heeled shoes encasing my frozen feet, and tried to hurry to decrease the distance between my friend and myself. Pain surged through my entire body. I needed a diversion to take my mind off my predicament.

That is when I noticed it.

There were millions of confetti-like things floating down from the sky. My heart began pounding in my chest from excitement. Something strange was happening around me, something entirely foreign to my tropic understanding. I tried to keep pace with my friend, who was now entering the hospital grounds. I tripped, steadied myself, and continued with as much haste as my frozen feet would allow.

By the time we reached the driveway that led to MacDougall House, white patches had begun to form on the road, on the grass at the sides of the driveway, on the branches of the trees, and all over our coats. The sky was now a low lying grey blanket, giving birth to millions of frozen wafers of water tumbling furiously earthward, then congregating in white heaps and mounds all around us.

I suddenly realised what was happening. June stopped and turned around to face me, her eyelashes dusted white.

" Snow!" we both shouted simultaneously in unrehearsed voices. We were experiencing our first snowfall! Fear and pain quickly gave way to exhilarating excitement.

We were familiar with the snow-scaped picture postcards which could be bought in Woolworth's on King Street. We were also familiar with snow scenes in movies we had watched. On our way from the train station three weeks before, we had seen the white capped mountains and hills in the far distance, and knew that white substance was snow. But this was different.

Snow, like cold, soft, damp feathers, was falling all around us, and we wanted to enjoy the wonder of it all.

* * * * *

June grabbed my gloved right hand, and we broke into a trot. We wanted to get indoors quickly and get warmed up so that we could come outside again, and properly enjoy the snow.

I stumbled and fell, my sprawled body making indentations in the soft, fallen snow. With my friend's help, I pulled my legs up, and positioned them so that I could stand. Then I noticed that I had no shoes on, and they were no where to be seen. I must have lost them back there on the Old North Road, when I had stumbled, and was, until now, unaware that the only thing separating my feet from the frozen pavement, was a pair of nylon pantyhose.

I don't quite remember what took place from the moment I discovered my swollen shoeless feet, to when I woke up in sickbay, seven hours later.

June said I had become hysterical, and ran like the dickens to the residence, where I was found a few minutes later, soaking my feet in the bath, in water " much too warm," and "the worse thing one can do," in the situation.

* * * * * *

Christmas morning found me, and my throbbing bandaged 'chilblained' feet, in bed, in the residence Sickbay. I looked out the large bay window at the beautiful white landscape which glistened from the golden glow of a high sun, and stretched for as far as my eyes could see. My eyes stung with the emergence of tears which formed rivulets down my cheeks.

Was I weeping because of the searing pain which was cutting through my legs and feet like a surgeon's scalpel? Or was it the sudden realization that I was thousands of miles across the Atlantic Ocean, away from the familiarity and warmth of my tropical home? Was it because I had found myself stranded as it were, and disabled on Christmas Day, in an environment which was hostile, though breathtakingly beautiful to behold?

Whatever the reasons for my tears, I knew without a doubt that this would be a Christmas I would not easily forget.

Walking Against The Wind

It is ten hundred hours on December 22nd, and the flurries which started at daybreak, have matured into a full-fledged blizzard. The wind bangs the neighbour's toolshed door which is making an awful racket.

With savage fury, it whips the snow against the window-pane, allows some of the flakes to stick, start melting, and then freeze.

My breath clouds the screen door as I peer outside to see if my husband Les has gotten the car started. He has, and beckons me to come out.

I don my toque, pulling it over my ears, and step outside locking the door behind me. The wind is raw and wild, and kicks angrily at my eyeballs, the only part of me presently sensitive to its rage. My eyes fill up and overflow. They always do that on sudden exposure to cold winds.

This is a god-awful day for anyone to be outdoors. I have to, though. It is very important for me to attend a meeting with the human rights officer scheduled for eleven hundred hours. I will learn then how I can or should proceed with my complaint against the nursing department of the hospital where I have worked for twenty-six years.

I hurry towards the Buick and enter,

enjoying its sheltered warmth. I brush the snow, that has followed me in, off my coat and take the car door back from the wind, slamming it shut.

"I'm glad I'm going down with you," Les says. "I wouldn't want you driving in this weather."

I smile at my husband, but he is looking behind him as he backs the car onto the street.

"As a matter of fact," he continues, "I'll try to be at all the meetings that you may have to attend. I don't want those bastards getting away with more than they have already."

"I know," I say, rubbing the frosted window with my gloved hand so that I can see outside. I relish the assurance Les offers.

" The officer mentioned on the phone that today we'd be going over my complaint point by point before the investigative inquiry can be scheduled." I lean back against the corduroy covered seat of the Buick and close my eyes against the fury of the storm.

"I guess it's gonna take a long time!" It is more a statement made than a question asked.

"These inquiries usually take forever," Les retorts, not taking his eyes off the road which is now piling up with snow. "But time shouldn't be a problem for us."

He honks the horn as some idiot in a blue Toyota races past us on our right and cuts in at a close shave just before the right lane merges. Les swears under his breath.

"You'd better concentrate on your driving," I suggest, noting that the storm is rapidly getting worse and the road more slippery.

I close my eyes again as the Buick inches its way down the Queen Street Hill. I am thinking that I should have been home doing my Christmas baking instead of being out in weather like this. But I know that I had started something which I was determined to see through to the end, no matter what that might be.

It was something that I should have done years before, but like many of the hospital's minority employees who had experienced some form of discrimination in the work place, I had delayed doing anything about it because of ignorance of the fact that something could be done, and maybe too from lack of courage.

Finally when the cup had overflowed, I had decided that enough was enough. If I did not do something, no one else would.

* * * * *

It had been evident from my arrival on the ward that the anglo-saxon supervisor did not like non-whites, and none stayed there for any length of time. Despite her humiliating tactics and efforts to undermine my work and head nurse position - many times in the presence of other personnel, I had stayed put, refusing to be forced out as others before and after me had been.

Then in March of 1979 I was informed by said supervisor that I was no longer a head nurse, but was back to general duty status. Although she said she had only just found out, there was evidence that she had known for three months, and had in fact been the instigator.

The Nursing Director never did inform me of the change in my position as was the protocol for such things.

71

As a general duty nurse on the same unit, I was most senior. I had my certificate in Midwifery (I had delivered over two hundred babies in Scotland, and one in said hospital). I also had certificates in Nursing Unit Administration and Effective Supervision as well as eleven years experience as a head nurse. Yet I was deliberately given junior duties to perform, left out of important ward meetings, not allowed to orientate new personnel and treated like a third class citizen.

It was now evident that the Supervisor had created a poisonous working atmosphere for me with the white staff members; and even the other non-white nurse was afraid, especially after being told by the Supervisor that we were not to work on the same shift or be seen conversing with each other on duty, by order of the Nursing Director.

The aim, it was voiced, was to rid the ward of all minority personnel, and since I refused to give in, life there had become almost unbearable.

Time had gone by with a third change of Nursing Director, one whom I thought would be sympathetic to the situation of minority nurses in the hospital, especially since it was said that she too was a minority although she did not look nor act like one.

Eventually the ward Supervisor-Head nurse retired and I had applied for the position. It was given to a junior nurse whom I had trained some years before, and who had neither the qualification nor experience I had. In fact evidence showed that she had applied for the position on prompting of the retired supervisor, two weeks after the competition had closed.

I was casually told by the Assistant

Nursing Director, responsible for that hiring, that my junior was given the position because she was going to do her Bsc.

This woman took over the ward and continued where her predecessor left off, but her hostility to non-whites (including student nurses, doctors and parents), was more open and intense. And as for me, open season was declared to the point where the staff was told to report anything I said or did while on duty.

I had begun to have severe headaches and insomnia from the stress of her constant harassment. Looking back, I can only equate the work environment with that of a lone lioness wandering into the habitat of a pack of wild dogs or hyenas.

But I was stubborn. I had refused to succumb to their desire for ethnic cleansing of the ward, and I suffered for it.

A few years later when a unit leader position was created on the ward, I had applied for it despite the fact that I was told by the Head Nurse in so many words that I need not bother.

A week after the farce, called an interview, which was really verbal abuse and unwarranted attack on my nursing performance, carried out in three parts over a period of a month, that evil little person – the devil in blonde disguise had posted the name of the successful applicant. This was her friend and sometimes babysitter, also junior to me in length of continuous service, qualification and experience.

That was when the rope finally snapped. All the bitterness and frustration, the anguish and embarrassment, the hurt and disillusionment of institutionalised discrimination suffered at the hands of people of my profession professing to be civilised, came to a head. I was committed to doing something about it.

No longer was I going to ignore the stress and pain these people had caused me, because to them I was not the right colour.

My human and civil rights had been violated. My professionalism was undermined, and I was going to do something about it at last.

None of the minority nurses I had spoken to over the years had given me any encouragement to complain. In fact they would not even back me up when I did. They thought I would be hitting my head against a brick wall, walking against the wind.

Of course, naturally they were trying to protect their jobs, and I could not quarrel with that.

That Tuesday afternoon in 1991 when I made contact with the Human Rights Officer, I knew that I was in for a very rough ride, given the racist climate of the day in many Canadian cities including Hamilton.

I knew it would be a difficult path to tread, but I had been walking on a road paved with live coals since I commenced working for the organization, and my feet had become immune to the heat and the pain.

I had made up my mind to expose the hospital's racist regime come what may, because they knew that discrimination existed (even to the way non-white patients were treated), and it was ignored.

* * * * *

I had sat across the desk from the Human Rights Officer after a short cordial greeting. I had handed him the manila envelope containing thirty-four pages of my life and times at the hospital, as he had requested on the phone a week before.

He had placed the envelope beside the stack of note paper before him without looking at its contents. From where I sat, I could make out only the date and time on the top page.

"Okay, I want you to tell me everything from the beginning."

He had leaned over to his right pressing a button on the phone and instructed the inquiring voice that he was not to be disturbed for about an hour, then returned his focus to me.

When I had first met him, I had been a bit apprehensive about how impartial he would be. After all he was white too. He might not even agree with me that the behaviour of my aggressors was discriminatory. But as I studied his features, I told myself that I would fight to the bitter end regardless, because I knew that what I was doing was right and warranted.

"Well," I had said making visual contact with his green eyes, "I don't know where to begin. My complaint is about a recent situation in which I applied for a new post on the ward and it was denied me. But actually the situation goes back much further than that." I had paused and moistened my lips with my tongue.

"When I mentioned on the phone about similar incidents which took place previously, you had thought that maybe it was too late to make a complaint about those." I had paused again, and marvelled at how strangely composed I felt.

75

"Even so," he had answered, leaning forward and tapping his pen lightly on his notepad. "If you start from the beginning I might be able to establish a pattern of behaviour, not just to you, but to other minority workers and each episode might be found to relate. I'll be making notes as you speak, and may interrupt you to ask a question or clarify a point, okay?"

"Okay!" I had retorted, and took him on the journey which began on May 17th, 1965, in that Hamilton hospital.

When I was through recanting I had leaned back in the chair feeling spent and angry. Just voicing some of the injustices I had endured had been enough to arouse anger in me.

"There you have it!" I had said, having just unburdened my mind. "What do you think?"

He had finished writing a few more words on the last page of his note pad, and placed his uncapped pen beside it. He had looked a bit as drained as I had felt.

"It will do," he had said with strong convictions. "All the incidents you mentioned are definitely connected, and it shows a pattern in the supervisor's attitude towards you."

He had glanced at his watch. The clock on the wall in front of me was saying 14.10 hours. I had taken an hour and ten minutes to relate. It had not seemed that long.

"But because you did not readily report any of the incidents before now," he had continued, " I will have to discuss it thoroughly with my boss, checking with the Human Rights Code to make sure we can go ahead with an investigation."

He had opened the envelope I had given

76

him at the beginning of the meeting, and after writing the date on the first sheet, pinned them to his own notes and placed them in his folder.

"Seems to me that you've been in a battle you must have felt you couldn't win. More like walking against the wind." He had stood up, stretched and sat down again.

"Walking Against The Wind!" I had thought. I had heard that phrase before.

"Yes, you're right." I had answered as I placed my handbag over my shoulder and stood up. "Though no one in his right mind would intentionally walk against the wind." I had licked my lips again, wishing I had brought my lip softener with me to do the job instead.

"But," I had continued, "if he finds himself doing so, he has two choices. He can go limp and let the wind propel him, push him, toss him about like a dust bunny in a vacuum cleaner. Submit to its mercy or slavery."

"And the other choice?" He had looked at me squarely with a hint of a smile. I knew from the amused look on his face that he jolly well knew what the second choice was. He had just wanted me to say it out loud.

"The other choice is," I had said, warming to the mood of the moment and even smiling a little, "to face the obstacle with determination and strength. Fine, he might be pushed back three paces for every pace he advances, but if he intends to get to his destination, he'll have to keep up the struggle. He'll eventually get there if it takes him twenty years."

"Or Twenty-six, no pun intended." He had stood up then and offered me his hand. "I admire your guts and determination. I will contact you as soon as I get the go ahead to start an

77

investigation if not for all of the complaints at least for the last one."

"Thank you, and good-bye." I had replied and walked out the door to the elevator.

We cannot find parking close to the Standard Life Building which houses the Human Rights Office, so Les decides to park in the City Hall parking lot. It means we will have to walk two blocks to our destination.

The snowfall is now a rip roaring blizzard, and the winds are stronger and more vocal. The windscreen and windows of the Buick are totally fogged up by the time we park it.

Les gets out first and promptly lands on his bottom, but is on his feet in a flash and holds my door open for me as I get out.

"God!" He says turning up the collar of his coat with his free hand, and attempting to close the door with the other. He succeeds on the third try. He vigorously brushes accumulated
snow from his beard.

"God!" he says again. "We've got to be out of our minds to be caught outside in weather like this!"

"You've said it." I reply, swallowing a mouthful of snow that forced its way in, and feeling somewhat guilty that I had not called and cancelled the appointment and re-book it for a more civilized day.

I hold onto my husband's arm for stability. He locks the car and does a quick eye check before leaving it.

We walk down the path, which in clement weather would be a few steps to Main Street, and cross to the north side. A teenaged girl dressed in light weight beige jacket runs past us in the pedestrian crossing, trying to catch a bus which has already moved away from the stop. I look back over my shoulder and see her rubbing the bare areas between her short skirt and knee high boots.

"How stupid," I think. "When will these kids learn to dress themselves properly?" And my mind races back to my youthful days of being stupid also where fashion was concerned.

"She's going to freeze if a bus doesn't come soon!" Only I know what I've just said. The frozen deformed words could not have been audible to anyone else.

"The wind is blowing from the east," Les says as thick fog rushes from his mouth and swirling snowflakes try to get in. "We'll be walking against it for two blocks. We'll be frozen stiff by the time we get there!"

As if eager to confirm my husband's prediction, a gush of wind rips my toque off my head and takes it across the street where it promptly keeps pace with a red Camaro.

I grab the hood of my coat and cover my snow dusted head, holding the tabs together under my chin. Chasing after the toque would not only be futile, but down right dangerous.

My thoughts quickly go back to the old North Road in Bellshill, Scotland, on that cold windy December day in 1964, when for the first time in my life I had experienced chilblains.

~That's because you were walking against the wind," Dr. Clarkson had said when he had examined my friend and I later that afternoon in the Nurses' Sick Bay. By then our hands and feet had thawed. Despite our painful and reddened fingers and toes, we had laughed uncontrollably at the word 'chilblains.' We had never heard of it before, and it surely had sounded funny when he said it in his deep Scottish accent.

I am suddenly seized with a strong desire to laugh, and do so, almost to the point of hysterics.

Les holds my hand a bit firmer, as if by doing so he'll be able to control my sudden onset of madness.

"What's the joke?" He shouts at me as we struggle to move forward on the now sparsely peopled pavement.

"Chilblains!" I shout back through my laughter, and quickly wipe wind-induced tears from my eyes so that I can see.

"Ah! Scotland!" He offers and joins me in laughter.

"Here I go again," I say in my mind. "I'm walking against the wind, but am also laughing; and laughter is the best medicine they say."

"Maybe today's the day I get cured," I say out loud without meaning to.

"Of what? Chilblains?" Les asks, not really expecting an answer.

We look at each other for a sober moment and start laughing again.

Contemplating Christmases Past.

It's Christmas, and unlike the rest
At home, I have a serious quest;
To look back into years long past,
A critical eye on each cast,
Each Christmas that I've known.
Examine each one in my mind,
Extract the good things I can find,
Re-live the happiness and bliss,
The joys of love and each small kiss,
And see how I have grown.

Or find perhaps a trouble spot
Somewhere, when I was just a tot,
Embraced in childish ignorance,
And like a kid, did buck and prance
And had a lot to say.
Or of the days when in my youth
I oft in jest did stretch the truth;
When I on Santa Clause had spied,
Or for my sibling's toys had cried,
And hoped to get my way.

Then as a teen, not quite matured
But old enough, from trivia cured;
When I wanted to change the world,
The flag of peace oft times unfurled
While I got torn and bruised.
Then moving to more mature things,
Mostly of the heart; those love flings;
Christmas romances I recall
Were usually the best of all,
For no one was ill used.

Yes, through the years I have matured,
From trivial faults I think I'm cured;
I try to see things clearer now
Though I still ask when, why and how
And still intend to do.
Each Christmas I mature and grow
In things about which I should know,
Like why at Christmas my heart sings
And treasures all the joy it brings,
The love and the peace too.

I contemplate Christmases past,
Knowing that memories will last;
For they are precious, treasured things,
So dear to me, like crowns on kings,
And so they will remain.

For Christmas then is Christmas now,
The story of Christ's birth somehow
Will live through ages, fostering love
Which first descended from above,
Forever here to reign.

'Twas The Night Before.

'Twas the night before Christmas,
and in the Lord's house
I sat rather contrite,
and quiet as a mouse;
For that's where the blizzard outside
forced me to go,
So I could escape
from the cold and the snow.

The naked pews gazed at me
with unseen eyes,
As I sat in the darkness,
a fool 'mongst the wise.
I felt lone and dejected,
a stranger, outcast,
So I looked in my mind
for Christmases of the past.

The wind which was howling
and blowing outside,
Made me shiver,
but glad for this safe place to hide.
All at once I felt comforted,
warmed and at peace,
And the turmoils
that were my thoughts, stilled;
the storm ceased.

I realised at that moment,
though far from my home,
God is with me in this place,
or wherever I roam.
Through the good times and bad,
in the calm or the storm,
If I let Him, He's with me
in whatever the form.

'Twas the night before,
and the old church – my safe place
Was a haven in which
I could feel the Lord's grace;

As it warmed and consoled me,
the bright light on the door
Made me think of the Christmas Star
on that night before.
It guided the wisemen
as they searched for the King,
And encouraged the angels
in heaven to sing.
Shining above the manger
of the holy boy
Who was sent by God
to bring peace, love and joy.

And that joy, 'midst the storms of life,
I found that night,
In the old church, quite alone,
but in the Lord's sight.
There He calmed my fears,
and I will always adore
The Lord, whom I met
on that stormy night before.

Two Faces Of Christmas.

Sonny

Sonny had joined the queue which extended west along Sutton to Orange Streets. His position in the extended line did not guarantee him getting into Bramwell Booth Memorial Hall in time for the Christmas concert, but he had hoped he would be lucky enough to receive a gift, no matter how trivial.

In his nine years of life he had never received a Christmas gift from anyone. His mother had been too poor to buy him any, and the meagre wages she received from working at Cherry Laundry as a laundress, was hardly enough to feed and clothe them, and pay the rent for the two room wood and stucco building they shared with Granny T.

In fact he had owned only seven pieces of outer clothing – the khaki shirt and pants which was his school uniform. A pair of cream serge long pants which the son of his mother's boss had outgrown and he had inherited along with a short sleeve white poplin shirt. And a long sleeved blue one which came with the pants. Also a pair of blue jeans cut off at the knees where there once were holes, and a black T shirt which his mother had bought for him at Nathan's Bargain bin two months before, and which he was wearing.

87

Sonny had learned to be very careful with his clothes so they would last for as long as possible. As a matter of fact, he had been careful with everything. If a piece of bread he was eating fell to the floor, he would pick it up, brush it off and eat it. Food in his household was not for wasting. His mother had taught him that.

She had also taught him never to come away from his classes with nothing learned. "Education will be your only ticket out of poverty," she used to tell him, mostly at times when she thought he was being distracted. "A good education will open windows of opportunity for you, and with God's help, even doors." She used to make that statement with such conviction, he had thought that she could see into the future.

That Christmas Eve he had come away from Bramwell Booth Memorial Hall with nothing. They had cut the line off fifteen people ahead of him. He had counted. They had explained that the hall could not hold any more.

Most of the children and their parents left outside had wandered off looking dejected, disappointed or angry, but two boys like himself had lingered at the door, hoping that it would open and they would be allowed inside. But it never happened.

Eventually the other boys had left and he was alone. His heart had felt like a stone in his chest, and his throat had tightened and threatened to restrict the amount of air that was sweeping his lungs.

He had hoped that at least this once he would be given a store bought toy, but it was not to be. The flood gates opened, and his tears had come crashing down his cheeks unchecked.

"They locked me out Mama," he had sobbed, as she held and tried to console him. "I didn't even get a candy."

"Don't worry Sonny," she had said convincingly, "you'll get something nice this Christmas. You'll see." And he had. He never knew what his mother had to forfeit in order to buy him that soccer ball, but his joy had been unspeakable.

Sonny remembered vowing to himself that when he grew up he would make sure that every poor child he knew would get a gift at Christmas, no matter how simple.

He had settled down and was very attentive to his lessons, and spent hours of almost every day in the local library as he availed himself of the required books he needed to study but could not afford to buy.

He had worked hard, and his mother's encouragement and expressed faith in him had paid off. He had won many scholarships and had graduated from the College of Arts, Science and Technology at Mona, as an engineer. Three years later he earned his B.Sc. in Economics from the University of the West Indies in Jamaica, and now ran his own engineering firm.

At thirty-one years of age, he had build his mother a house in Barbican, and lavished her with the things of life which she had gone without when they were poor.

Donald 'Sonny' Ellis was forty-six now, with a wife and family of two. His mother had died of Leukaemia two years ago, and he had just now officiated at the opening of the hall he had built in her memory – The Sarah Ellis Memorial Hall.

It was Christmas Eve, bright, sunny and

promising. Sonny stood by the front door of the hall and watched the unending line of children (some with their parents), enter and receive their bags of cookies, candies, a basket of groceries and a store bought toy, then leave through one of the side doors so as to keep the line moving.

The front door was left open until the last child had entered and received his gifts. Sonny smiled and said to himself "This is a good beginning."

* * * * *

Manuel

The Midwife, Mary Barnes removed her examining fingers from the vagina of the young mother-to-be. She stripped the gloves from her hands and placed them on the tray at the foot of the bed. She was conscious of the two pairs of eyes watching her every move.

"Is everything alright Nurse? Is the baby okay?" The anxious father fixed his steel blue eyes on the midwife's face, willing them to read her mind.

"Am I dilating...." The wife's question was cut off in mid-sentence as she was enveloped in another wave of contraction which now came more frequently and with great intensity.

"Aye," replied the midwife, looking from the husband to his wife and back to the husband where her gaze rested.

"Mr. MacPherson, your wife is fully dilated, and has been so for twenty minutes now. The baby's face is forward and the head is not

90

flexing into the position necessary for its birth. I'll have to take her into the hospital to be on the safe side."

"Oh, dear God!" Bob MacPherson uttered in an almost whispered voice. "Is there anything you can do, anything you can give her to help? We would rather not go to hospital if at all possible." He knelt by the side of the bed and held his wife's hand as she began to bear down with the mounting contractions.

It was evident that she had entered the second stage of labour, and was becoming very distressed. The midwife listened to the foetal heart with her stethoscope resting gently on Elizabeth's lower abdomen. Another contraction started, and the patient was encouraged to bear down.

"A quick breath now Hon, and push down again into your bottom," the midwife coaxed and the patient complied, then rested as the contractions subsided.

The Midwife tried again to locate the baby's heartbeat, and this time she counted it for a full minute ahead of the next contraction. It was slower and irregular now. The baby was getting into trouble.

"Elizabeth, I'm going to examine you again," she announced washing her hands in the basin of clean water the husband had brought in after the last examination. "We'll see if the baby has moved down any, and take it from there."

Nurse Barnes had already informed the doctor by phone, of the impending emergency, and he had summoned the Emergency Flying Squad as well as alerting the nearest Maternity Hospital.

The midwife prayed silently as she

examined the patient, that everything would go well tonight for this couple.

* * * * * *

They had been her patients through their first, and second pregnancies, as well as this one. Bob MacPherson a secondary school teacher was from the Glasgow area. He had lost his first wife of three months in an automobile accident, and had remarried ten months afterwards.

Elizabeth was from Dunoon and worked as a travel consultant at a travel agency here in Airdrie, near where they lived. Their first pregnancy had ended at twenty-six weeks gestation when the placenta (the afterbirth), had separated from the uterine wall and she miscarried.

Mrs. MacPherson had become pregnant again six months after her miscarriage, and the couple in happiness looked forward to having a baby at last. At thirty-eight weeks gestation after a normal and healthy pregnancy, Elizabeth had gone into labour and was admitted to the local Maternity hospital.

Her labour had progressed well until she entered the second stage. The foetal heart had suddenly dropped to below eighty beats per minute, and continued to fluctuate. The Obstetrician had intervened and applied forceps to deliver the baby as quickly as possible. Their baby daughter had been born dead, "a fresh stillbirth" was the term used.

The MacPhersons had grieved loudly and long, and had vowed not to go into a hospital again if they could help it. Not that they had blamed the hospital for the disastrous outcomes of the two pregnancies, but for them it stood as a place of 'bad luck'.

At Elizabeth's first visit to the pre-natal clinic when she discovered she was pregnant for the third time, she had made it quite clear to Nurse Barnes and the doctor, that she wanted to deliver at home. Although she was considered at 'high risk' with a 'bad obstetrical history' and should be delivered in hospital, she had insisted on a home delivery. However she had also promised that she would consent to going into hospital if the need arose.

The midwife could see deep concern on the face of Bob MacPherson as he coaxed his wife through her fast coming contractions. He swabbed her face with a cool wash cloth and tried to get her mind in tune with the idea of going to the hospital.

"I think for the wain's sake we should do what Nurse has suggested, lass."

Elizabeth seized by another contraction, grabbed her husband's hand, squeezing mercilessly as she bore down hard.

The midwife opened the patient's legs and introduced her examining gloved fingers. "God love us!" she exclaimed trying to keep her excitement in check. "The head is down in the birth canal. Come on Hen, push. You still have a contraction. Push, push, push!"

"Ahhhhhh!" Elizabeth screamed, trying to breathe and pant at the same time, and unable to resist the urge to bear down.

"It's okay lass. You're doing great sweetheart," her husband soothed. And her membranes ruptured and flooded the bed.

The baby's round face appeared facing upwards, and a jubilant midwife slipped its anterior shoulder out as the rest of the pink body followed. He had a lusty cry.

"Here is your son," the midwife said smiling with relief as she placed the tiny bundle on his mother's chest. "Mother, you did very well, and so did you, Dad."

As she continued the routine care of her two patients, the midwife thanked God in her heart for the safe delivery of a healthy child to the anxious and frightened parents, in their own home as they had wished.

An hour later after the doctor was informed, the emergency ambulance cancelled, the delivery instruments cleared away and the bedroom put back in order, Nurse Mary Barnes handed the newborn, now washed and dressed and bundled, to his parents.

As she sipped the freshly brewed tea Bob MacPherson had made, she looked at the beaming faces of the happy parents with the babe nestled between them, and thought on the manger scene in Bethlehem, on this day, so very long ago.

"What time was he born Nurse?" the young mother asked sounding tired but too excited to sleep.

The midwife looked at her watch. It said 1:20 a.m. – December 25th.

"He was born at fourteen minutes after midnight," she retorted. "He's a Christmas boy."

"Then we'll call him Manuel," the husband announced smiling at his wife.

"Yes. His name is Manuel Barnes MacPherson," said the wife as she looked adoringly into the face of her sleeping Christmas child.

Santa – The Imposter

They walked through Sears from the back parking lot and headed out into the open mall by way of the upper concourse. They stopped simultaneously, leaned against the railings across from Shoppers Drug Mart, and looked down on the Santa village below.

Santa was holding a little blonde girl in red plaid on his knee. He was smiling, saying something to her, but she did not appear to be amused. The clown stretched across Santa and handed her a candy-cane which she hurriedly started to unwrap.

There were many children in line waiting to see Santa, most of them appearing somewhat restless.

"I wonder how many of them he's going to tell not to come back to see him because they are too old?" The son looked at his mother, and then with a bemused smile on his face scanned again the scene below and added "But then there aren't any black kids in the line, are there?"

The woman looked at her son, and the incident of thirteen years ago unfolded again before her eyes.

"Oh my God!" she thought. "He still remembers that awful December day, in this same place, and about the same time!"

It was not an easy thing to forget. She certainly had not forgotten, but she thought

95

that he had, since it was never mentioned after the furore of that day. It was thought that the sour note of that Christmas time had been left behind him, giving way to childhood growth and development, and many more happier memories. But at twenty years of age, and on the threshold of manhood, his recessed thoughts had been brought to the fore and put into words.

"You remember that incident?" She asked looking at him in amazement.

He returned his mother's gaze and replied. "Sure I remember. I never forgot it. I didn't talk about it, but I always wondered what I had done to cause Santa to be so mean to me. It pacified me somewhat though", he smiled widely, remembering, "when you said that the santa was an imposter, hence his bad behaviour to me. But I still felt that I had been a bad boy, for him to treat me that way."

He looked again at the gathering below. A little boy in a Blue Jays baseball cap and monogrammed jacket was now sitting on Santa's knee. His older sibling waited beside the clown for her turn.

"Mind you," the son chuckled and moved his gaze back to his mother, "I learned quickly, and in varying degrees, that there are many such Santas in the world in the form of my peers, bus drivers, store attendants, teachers..." He paused then briefly glanced down at his watch.

" I'll never forget that teacher in grade nine who couldn't understand, or wouldn't," he chuckled again, "why I refused to study or take part in the discussion of the book 'To Kill A Mockingbird'. She couldn't understand why the only non-white student in the class would risk failing English that term, rather than contribute to his own humiliation at the hands of his classmates and herself."

"And then again," he continued as they walked on towards Eaton's, "for every despicable 'Santa,' there are many who are honourable members of the human race who see me for who I am and not for what I look like."

The mother glanced with surprise and admiration at her son. How many times as he grew, she had seen her own determined strength mirrored in his eyes? She had fought many unjust battles from when she was as young as he is, after venturing out into new lands among new people and new cultures. She could remember each incident plainly, always with rage and resentment. And she remembered that Christmas time.

* * * * *

The day had opened brilliantly fine. The sun shone from a cloudless sky, and there was enough frost in the air to convince everyone that it was indeed December.

She had been doing some last minute shopping with her seven year old in tow. The atmosphere of the mall had been festive, and Santa was in attendance at his 'village'.

The mother had never before taken her child to see any of the santas in the malls. There had been no specific reason why she hadn't.

He had been to many private Christmas parties and seen Santa there. Today he was pleading with her to let him 'go see Santa' and since there were only a few children waiting in line, she had given in and took her son over to the 'village'.

When it was his turn, her son had walked
in on his own while she waited outside the
enclosure. Santa's smile had faded as the child
approached. He did not put the boy on his knee.
He had said something at which the boy had
immediately hung his head and walked away
without taking the candy-cane the clown at the
gate was offering him.

He had taken his mother's hand and
walked briskly a little ahead of her.

Sensing that something was wrong, she
had asked what the matter was. "What did Santa
say, honey?" the mother had asked as they both
got into the car.

The child had broken down then into
uncontrollable sobs. "He told me to get away from
him. That I was too old to come wasting his time
asking for toys. I only want a 'Battleship
Galactica'." He had buried his face in his hands
and continued sobbing. "Santa hates me
Mommie," he had wept.

The mother had taken him into her arms
and rocked him, as anger surged up in her like
molten lava and made her want to explode.

"That santa is an imposter honey," she
had heard herself utter, trying to keep her
anger in check in order to placate her child.
Instantly she had known that she could not let
him get away with humiliating her child. Of
robbing him of that look of joy and anticipation
that was in his eyes before he was shot down by
his bitter stinging words.

"Sweetheart," the mother had said softly,
cupping the child's face in her hands. "will you
come back with Mommie so that I can have a word
with the imposter?" The little boy had bravely
nodded 'yes'. They had walked back briskly

through Sears, and down the stairs to Santa's Village.

A boy about ten or eleven had been sitting on Santa's knee. Both had been smiling. There had been a flash from a camera, and the clown was handing him a candy-cane, as the irate mother, still holding onto her son's hand, entered.

"Merry Christmas! Ho! Ho!..." Santa was cut off by the young mother's question.

"How old do you think that boy is who just got off your knee, Santa?" the woman had asked in a stern but well controlled voice.

"Oh, he says he's eleven," the imposter had answered and had looked with recollection at the child at her side. "Why?"

"Because," she had said in a voice much louder but still controlled, "a few minutes ago you insulted my child. You told him to get away from you and stop wasting your time. That he was too old to be coming to you and asking for toys." The place had suddenly become quiet, so that if a pin had fallen to the floor it would have been heard.

Santa had stood up seeming very uncomfortable. His colour had flushed red.

"Why did you humiliate my child and rob him of the joy Christmas is supposed to bring to children? Is it because he doesn't look like you?"

Santa had blushed again and opened his mouth to say something, but the mother had not allowed him to.

" He is seven years old, Santa." She had said the name with disdain. "Yes seven, and I will not let you get away with what you have done. I am reporting the matter to the manager of this mall and to the news media." She had walked away with her child, and so did the other parents there.

"Imagine saying something like that to a child and at Christmas!" she had heard someone say. The Santa had tried at some lame excuse, but the mother had walked away without looking back. She had felt somewhat justified in taking the stand she had.

She and her husband had done a lot that day to try to help erase the awful event from their child's mind.

* * * * *

The woman came out of her reverie and found that they were in Eaton's, and the young man was holding a sweater up against himself awaiting her comments.

"You seemed as if you were in deep thoughts, Mom," he offered as the salesperson wrapped his purchase. "You weren't thinking back to that day, were you?"

"That boy could always read my mind," she thought. "Yes, I was," she admitted.

"Mom," he said putting his arm around her shoulder. "incidents like those you should remember only in jest, especially if you had dealt with it satisfactorily, which you had. Once you have confronted it, and dealt with it, you owe it to yourself to move away from it. Hey, you can remember, but not with bitterness."

The mother gazed at her son, twenty years old going on sixty. He looked and sounded so wise! She wished that she could glean some of that wisdom.

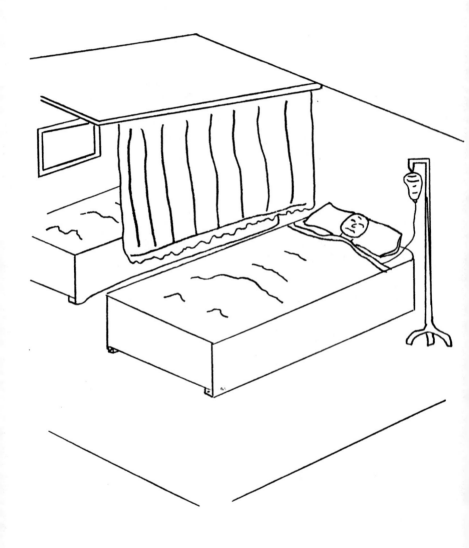

A Gift For Freddie

Allyne walked quickly along the corridor of the ward towards Room 4B. The ward clerk talking on the phone at the Nurses' Station acknowledged her with a smile as she passed. She could hear soft jerky laughter – baby laughter, coming from the room as she approached it. Her heartbeat quickened, and a warm excited feeling flooded her being. It was the same feeling she had had two and a half months ago when she found out that she was indeed compatible and would be able to donate bone marrow to her tiny goddaughter.

She had been unavoidably absent at the child's initial transfusion, having been called away to attend an uncle's funeral in the Caribbean. She would be seeing her goddaughter for the first time in three weeks, although she had been brought up-to-date about her progress on the phone.

She entered the small, well lit room and took in the scenery. The little patient was the happiest she had seen her since her birth. Both arms were splinted, and into the left dripped life from a bag hanging from the pole attached to the side of the crib.

The red fluid that was coursing through the tubing and canula into the baby's tiny vein, was from her own body.

The nurse, who was gently tickling Freddie, straightened up and smiled at the newcomer. The baby's gaze moved briefly to the nurse half expecting to be tickled some more, then lingered on the happy face of her godmother.

Freddie's angelic smile widened and shone through her big brown eyes. She instinctively put out her arms though somewhat hampered, begging to be picked up.

Allyne felt relieved that her three week absence had not interfered with the baby's memory of her.

"Hi, Nurse Brown," she said moving towards the crib and picking the baby up.

"Hi, Allyne," replied the nurse checking the infusion bag and needle site briefly. "You just missed her grandparents. They've gone for lunch I think. Doesn't she look great?" She tussled freddie's short black curls and walked towards the door.

"She certainly does," Allyne replied holding the child closer and kissing her on the forehead. "Is it okay if I hold her a bit?" Being a nurse herself, she knew the importance of not overtaxing a patient's strength, especially one who was as ill and as fragile as Freddie.

"Oh yes! Go ahead," was the reply. "Cuddling won't harm her, and she is much stronger now. That is her third bag you know?" She added as she left the room.

Allyne sat in the oversized arm chair with Freddie nestled closely in her arms. "Hi sweetheart," she said kissing her once more, and the brown eyes closed into comforting sleep.

The godmother studied the features of the sleeping child. The soft olive complexion, the thick black eyebrows which almost met in the middle, and the long black lashes, slightly curled at the ends. She did indeed look less fragile, healthier. She even felt heavier.

Allyne felt a strong bond towards this child. Stronger than is usual between a godparent and godchild. It was as if she had given birth to her. It was a blood-bond, and she remembered how it had started.

* * * * *

The day had opened brilliantly fine. The golden sun had been sitting high in a pristine blue sky when she left for work that Thursday in July, seventeen months ago.

The Neonatal Unit where Allyne had just begun her afternoon shift was unusually quiet. The intensive-care section was empty, and there were only four newborns on intravenous therapy, two of them requiring minimal amount of oxygen to keep them pink.

The transitional section had four, awaiting final routine examinations before being transferred to their mothers. And the graduated-care section had two babies in open cots, getting used to maintaining their own body temperatures before being discharged home. Two other full term babies were there receiving phototherapy for physiological jaundice.

"I can't believe this is the same ward we left last night, after running ragged the entire shift," Selma, the part-time nurse had said to no one in particular. She had been moving from cot to cot replenishing the bedside tables with linen.

"Enjoy it while you can," Allyne had retorted, knowing from her twenty-five years

105

experience on the unit that a census of twelve and a quiet ward would not last very long. "This is the calm before the storm. I'll call Labour and Delivery to see what they have...."

"Damn and blast! You guys come and look at this." Mary the other full time nurse was examining one of the transitional-care babies, checking the respiratory rate. The wide-eyed baby boy had been plastered from the waist down in the thick green sticky stool of the newborn called meconium.

"My God! When will these doctors learn to replace the kids' diapers after they've examined them?" Selma had said after glancing at the mess.

Mary had wheeled the crib to the bath sink and commenced bathing the baby who had howled at the top of his lungs in protest. The Obstetrician on call was being paged on the P.A. system. The voice sounded urgent Allyne had noted.

Shortly afterwards, the phone on the south side of the unit had rung. Her adrenaline had started pumping as she lifted the receiver. And then all hell had broken loose.

* * * * *

It had been Emergency Room reporting that they had a seriously injured, pregnant woman there and needed an intensive-care isolette and nurse at once. The paediatrician was already there.

Allyne had repeated out loud what was being said on the phone, as she usually did, so that the others could hear what it was all about and start the ball rolling. They did.

"What a team!" she had thought as she wheeled the cumbersome isolette out the door and onto the elevator. On the ground floor the emergency room porter had met them and took charge of the front end of the machine as they sped towards their destination.

"God! Here we go again!" She had not had an easy shift for the last three months, and was looking forward to four weeks vacation starting the next day. She was going on a guided tour of Alaska with her friends Lucille and Gerry Barnes.

Lucille had been her childhood friend since grade 8, and when she married Gerry he became an extended part of the friendship. In fact she had been more like a member of their family. And come October 12th or there about, their only child Sandra, her goddaughter, would be a mother herself.

Allyne had smiled at the prospect of perhaps being godmother to her goddaughter's child.

They had now entered the Emergency Room which was like paddy's market. There were people and equipment everywhere. A door had swung open in the short corridor and Dr. Neil, the paediatrician, had grabbed the front of the isolette and pulled it halfway into the room.

The baby was already born, incubated and being bagged by the anaesthetist. She was limp and blue – a tiny lump surrounded by a sea of green operating room sheets and towels.

Allyne had opened the tray for the umbilical catheterization and assisted with the procedure, soon after she had received an intravenous infusion of ten per-cent glucose, going in a scalp vein, after three tries.

The baby had been placed in the oxygen flooded isolette, and transported to the Neonatal Unit where her resuscitative care continued.

Within two hours of being placed on the respirator, the baby's condition had begun to stabilize. Her colour was pink with dusky extremities. Activity and tone were fair, and heart rate had ranged between 100 and 208 beats per minute. The baby was being readied for transfer to the regional neonatal hospital.

After making the necessary arrangements for x-rays and blood specimens from both baby and mother, Allyne had sat down to do her charting on twenty-six weeks gestation Baby Girl Jones.

"What a coincident!" she had thought. Her goddaughter was married to Frederick Jones, and was about six months pregnant, but she lived in New Market!

There had been sketchy details about the baby. The father had died on the spot. The mother had died on arrival in the Emergency Room, and a Caesarean Section had been done on the spot in an effort to save her foetus. The police were trying to locate the next-of-kin.

By 10:40 p.m., the tiny patient was being transferred to MUMC (as the regional hospital was called), by their transport team. Allyne thought she would take a last look at the child they had worked so hard to save before she left, but the phone had rung. It had been the Emergency Room nurse. Baby Jones' next-of-kin were Lucille and Gerry Barnes of 60 Summit Drive, in Hamilton. They were the parents of the baby's mother.

She had dropped the phone and turned to face the paediatrician who had just got up from the desk.

"It's my goddaughter!" she had said looking at Dr. Neil without really seeing him. "The baby's mother was my godchild! Oh my God! Oh my God! Oh my God!" She had stumbled to the scrub sink and vomited. The doctor and one of her colleagues had come to support her, suggesting that she should go and lie down for a bit. After all none of them had had a break since coming on duty.

But she knew she had to be strong for her friends. They had lost their child and son-in-law, and their grandchild's life was hanging by a thread.

"I have to be there for them," she had said, and they had understood.

The next few weeks were hard and stressful. She had done her best in trying to console her friends, helping them with funeral arrangements (Fred's only relative was an aunt who lived in North Bay), and spending hours at Freddie's bedside assisting in her care as much as she was allowed. She had rotated hours with the grandparents so that one of them was almost always at the baby's bedside.

For the next six months they had travelled a roller coaster highway with Freddie. Her condition would seem to improve, she would be weaned off the respirator, then put back on again because of frequent apnoeic spells (periods when the child would stop breathing and turn blue). This had happened four times, and were very heart breaking for the family and frustrating for the care givers.

Freddie had had a few small blood transfusions for her anaemia which at first was thought to be due to the many blood testings which were needed and were done.

At last at age six-and-a-half months, she had been improved enough to go home to her family which included Allyne. On her friends' insistence, she had moved in with them for the first three weeks of the baby coming home. Allyne was sure that they were apprehensive about the apnoea monitor which Freddie needed at home, but she did not mind.

Although the baby remained pale and lethargic, her godmother knew that as a preemie baby she would take time to catch up. She just needed patience and a lot of love which she did get.

Then one night while on duty, Allyne had received a call from Gerry. They had just taken the baby to emergency where she was being admitted.

"She started choking, then vomited and went blue – no black!" He had sounded as though stifling a sob. Her heart ached for him. He had suffered through the tragedy of the deaths, and the pain, worry and concern for his grandchild, yet was never seen to cry or show his grief. He was living by the unspoken rule that men should show strength in times like these.

"Hogwash!" thought Allyne. "Go ahead and grieve openly like Lucille and I have done, and are doing." Aloud she had said "Gerry, why don't you go back and stay with Lucille, and I'll call the ward and find out what's going on, then get back to you?"

"Okay Allyne," his voice had sounded more controlled then. "I'll talk to you later. We'll be here for the rest of the night."

She had barely been able to finish her shift, then had gone to the paediatric ward to be with her friends – her family. Yes they were her family.

Her parents lived in the Bahamas, as did Lucille's. Her only brother lived in London, England, and although she had a boyfriend, they had not made any commitments to each other. She was forty-three years old, owned her apartment, had a wonderful profession and a secure, though stressful job. She was on her own, except for the Barnes who made her feel a part of their family.

At 10:15 that morning, the doctor had walked into the room with news as bleak as the day. Lucille had been rocking Freddie gently back and forth as she lay sleeping in her arms. Freddie was looking pale as death and just as fragile. Allyne and Gerry had stood up as the doctor entered. He had smiled, a plastic smile she thought. The kind one associates with bad news.

"Hi folks, I'm David Lang. I'll be treating Freddie for the next little while." He had averted his eyes for a moment, scanning the intravenous bag dripping glucose solution into Freddie's vein. His eyes had met each of theirs then latched onto Allyne's. His face had become serious.

"Is something wrong with the baby doctor?" Lucille's voice had sounded hollow and detached. "What's wrong?"

"I'm afraid it's not good news Mrs. Barnes." He had looked briefly at each of them again, and started leafing through the chart in his hand. "We've discovered that Freddie has a rare blood disorder which can only be treated by a bone marrow transplant from someone who is compatible."

They had gasped simultaneously, and

111

Gerry had broken down.

"Jesus Christ Almighty!" he had shouted, tears rolling down his cheeks and into his greying beard. All his reservations had vanished. "How much of this god–damn crap are we expected to take?" He was bawling like a baby, his hands covering his face.

"I'm sorry," Dr. Lang had said, pressing the call bell for a nurse. "I could talk to you all later when you're a bit more composed. I know it's tragic news to be imparting, but you need to know."

"We want to know, Doctor, we have to, regardless." Lucille had one arm around her husband's neck as he sobbed on her shoulder.

"Yes, go ahead Doc. I'm sorry for the outburst." Gerry had straightened up and had dried his face with his hands. All eyes had focused on the doctor's.

Allyne had remained silent and resolute. "It was good that Gerry had cried a little," she had thought. "He needed to."

The doctor had explained Freddie's haemological condition and the bleak outcome to them. If she did not get a bone marrow transplant as soon as possible, she would die. He had assured them that the test results were accurate – they had been repeated three times to make sure.

From then on it had been physical, mental and emotional hard work for the family. They had lived through long waiting periods, hoping for a donor for Freddie after the grandparents' disappointing test results.

The child's first birthday had come and gone quietly. She had been very ill in hospital and her family had been preoccupied about her pending death.

And then one day amidst her mental turmoil, Allyne had had a though. "What if I can be a donor? Why shouldn't I go and be tested?" She might not be a blood relative, she had thought, but one never knows. And even if it turned out that she was incompatible, she would feel better having tried to do something to help.

She mused over the thought for a week or so and then made up her mind.

* * * * *

The phone had rang just as she had stepped out of the shower. It was a warm October Monday, a week before Thanksgiving. A crow sitting atop a maple tree by her bedroom window, was calling incessantly to its mate, which could be heard answering in the distance.

She had picked up the phone on its third ring, water still dripping from her body.

"Hello?" She had said.

"Hello," the voice had sounded upbeat. "Is this Allyne Sampson?"

"Yes, it is," she had replied.

"Allyne, I have wonderful news!" The male voice had said, then went on to explain that she had been found to be compatible and therefore could donate bone marrow to her godchild.

By the time she had hung up she had been so overcome with emotion that she was forced to lie down for a while to gain some composure. She had thought of the pain she had experienced when they did the sampling, and what lay ahead, but she knew that it was and would be all worthwhile. She would be saving the little one's life.

Now two months later, Freddie was getting her third and last transfusion. Tests performed after the first two had shown great improvement in her condition. In fact it was noticeable in her improved colour, activity, alertness and appetite.

Allyne tenderly kissed the little round nose, and the eyelids flew open. Large brown eyes gazed into hers for a moment, then closed again.

She tenderly set the child down in her cot and straightened herself up. A baritone voice from a radio or television across the hall was singing *O Little Town of Bethlehem.*

"Oh my goodness!" Allyne said out loud scanning the stuffed animals on the bedside table and window ledge, as she raised the side of the crib. "It's three days before Christmas and I haven't even bought Freddie's gift yet. I better get going."

"Oh! but you have already given it to her," came a voice from behind. Lucille, Gerry and Doctor Lang entered. It was the first she had seen them in three weeks, and the happiest she had seen her friends in almost eighteen months.

"You have given Freddie back her life," Lucille said, hugging Allyne. "What Christmas gift can top that?"

"She's right," the doctor retorted moving closer to the crib. "This little girl is alive because of you. Christmas came early for her, and just in time. And how is my brown-eyed wonder?" He bent over the bedrails and tussled the curls of the child who was awake and looking in turn at her visitors.

"Mommie!" she cried, and gazed at her

114

grandmother, then at Allyne. They both moved towards her, then Allyne stepped back and allowed Lucille to respond.

"Hi sweetie!" she cooed to her granddaughter. "You look great. Doesn't she look great?"

"She sure does," her husband replied, taking her from his wife.

"So great," the doctor replied, "that you can have her home tomorrow. I'll go and write some orders now. I'll be on call over the Christmas holidays if you need me."

"Thank you Doctor!" They replied in unison.

"This Christmas is special." Gerry said almost reverently. "We have been given a wonderful gift, and Freddie, you are that gift." The baby gurgled some baby talk on hearing her name.

"It's as if she is reborn." Lucille added. "As if we're all reborn. Thank you God! Thank you Allyne!"

"Yes," answered Allyne, picking up her purse and moving towards the door. "We've all been born again." And she left to buy a gift for Freddie.

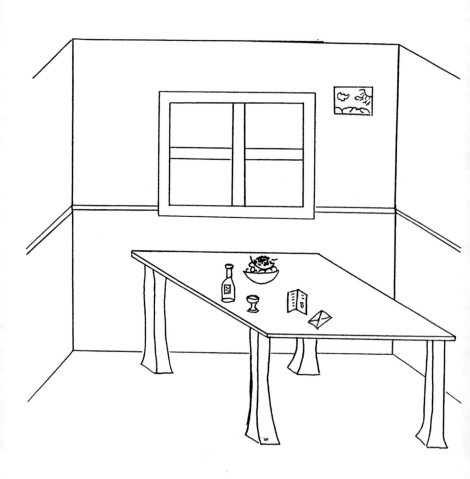

Of Christmas Cards and Rum Punch

The sun was like a liquid orb suspended in the low grey clouds. Afternoon was merging quickly into evening on the cold December day. I stopped the car at the entrance of the Emergency Room, got out and walked around to the passenger side of the Dodge. Nellie was already out and holding her nose. Dee had an arm around her shoulder supporting her.

"I'm alright," Nellie said for the hundredth time since we left the apartment. She released her nose for a second. It was now swollen and discoloured.

"You shouldn't have bothered to bring me here. The ice pack would have done the job in time. They're going to die laughing when they hear how I bumped my nose." She was trying to laugh through her pain.

"It's best for it to be x-rayed to make sure it isn't broken," Dee said, helping her through the doors and into the Emergency Room.

"I'll go park the car and then join you," I said to their backs, moving the Dodge out to allow a taxi to take its place.

I drove across the street into the parking ramp using my parkcard, and parked on the ground level. The ramp was sparsely occupied, afterall it was 17:00 hours on Christmas Eve.

117

Most of the patients were sent home on a short leave for Christmas day, therefore not many visitors were visiting. And the hospital was operating on a skeleton staff.

I parked the car beside the pay booth, and ran back across the street ahead of the Upper Sherman bus.

The ER was unusually quiet. There were five patients including Nellie, one of whom was lying on a stretcher, just coming back from, or going somewhere.

Nellie was lying on a stretcher in Room 3, with Dee standing beside it reading her chart. It was obvious from their conversation that a nurse had already been in to see her.

"Are they gonna order an x-ray?" I asked starting to read the chart too, without getting much information from it.

"We'll see if its necessary after I've examined the patient," was the reply behind me. An interne whom I did not recognise entered the room, his white lab coat flapping in torrents of air created as he walked. He went over to Nellie and touched her nose. She winced.

"Well, how did you sustain this injury?" he asked, taking the opthalmoscope out of its holder on the wall and directing its light towards her nostrils. "Been in the sauce again, have you?" He chuckled loudly. Dee's eyes met mine and we turned them towards Nellie. She laughed out loudly, then quickly checked herself, wincing with pain.

"Well Doctor," she tried to laugh again, "It's a simple matter of Christmas cards and rum punch, and the fact that I do not drink." She rolled over onto her side and touched her nose protectively.

118

"That sounds interesting," the doctor replied with an 'I know the score' smile on his face. He picked up the chart and scribbled away for awhile, the smile never leaving his face.

"Well?" he asked looking from Nellie to Dee and I and back again to Nellie. "What happened?"

"Well," our friend began haltingly, and all eyes focused on her face.

* * * * *

We had known Nellie for three and a half years, ever since we came to Canada. She was one of the first persons to befriend us when we joined the choir at the United Church which was close to where we lived.

"Hi," she had said to us at our first choir practice attendance. "Welcome, my name is Nellie Hughes. I'm an alto. Are you?" Her smile had radiated genuine warmth and friendliness, something we had experienced rarely since our arrival in the city four months before.

"I am Lynette Searles, and this is Dee Sawyer," I had said, offering my hand. "We sing soprano." Dee had added, offering hers.

We had readily become friends with Nellie, and did a lot together. The fact that she was twenty years our senior didn't really matter. She was fun to be with, very frank, a bit of a dare-devil, and had a wonderful sense of humour. She invited us to her home for corn roasts and barbecues, and introduced us to her family and the game of hockey which her teenaged son played, also the Royal Winter Fair in Toronto.

I remember once while we were visiting her at her home, she decided to show us an area

119

on her thigh which was bruised from being thrown by an unruly horse (she was an avid rider and at one time owned her own horse). In the process of casually disrobing to reveal the offending area on her anatomy, we noticed that the living room in which we were, faced the street and the drapes were opened. She was standing in full view of whoever chanced to look in.

"Nellie!" I had offered, while Dee stood shielding her from view. "People walking along the street will see you."

"That will serve them right for looking," she had said with a grin and continued to show off her bruise unhurriedly.

Unlike her husband she was always willing and eager to try new foods, so whenever she visited our apartment alone, we would make dishes like curried goat, escovitched fish, and rice and peas. She loved Jamaican patties and carrot juice. Like ourselves, Nellie did not drink, and getting her tipsy was the furthest thing from our minds when she dropped in on us that Christmas Eve.

We were on a six day break, including Boxing Day and the day after, and had invited Dee's Brother, his wife and two children, as well as an unmarried girlfriend to have Christmas dinner with us. Dee's brother Percy loved rum punch, so we had decided to make some for the festive occasion.

I had been filling the third and last bottle with the strawberry coloured beverage when the door buzzer sounded. Dee was talking on the phone, so I had quickly dried my hands and pressed the intercom button.

"Hi," came Nellie's voice through the

120

speaker, cheerful as always. "I'm glad you girls are in. I was just passing by. Can I come up?"

"Sure, come on up," I had said, and pressed the button to let her in the front door. "it's Nellie," I had said to Dee as she put the receiver down. "She's coming up."

"I wonder where she's off to now?" Dee had smiled.

"We'll soon find out," I had answered as she went to open the door.

Our friend entered, warmly clad, and wearing a holly wreath pin on her coat collar. Her grey-black hair, curled upwards, showed below her fur-trimmed hat. Her cheeks were rosy pink as they usually are in whatever the weather, and her blue eyes sparkled with mirth as she tested the air with her nose.

"Smells like a brewery in here," she had said, and walked past us to the sofa removing her ankle length boots in the process. "What are you up to? What are you making? Can I have a look?"

We had let her finish her questioning before attempting to respond, having learned over the years we had known her that it was better that way.

"I've just finished making Jamaican rum punch," I had replied, walking back into the kitchen to clean up, and put away the brew. She had followed me into the kitchen, and so did Dee.

"I thought you girls didn't drink? Gosh! it looks attractive in those bottles! How do you make it? Gee that rum smells awfully strong."

"We don't drink. We made it for our Christmas dinner guests," both Dee and I voiced simultaneously. Nellie moved towards the uncorked bottle lifting it up and sniffing its contents.

"It does smell strong. Can I taste it?" Dee and I looked at each other and then at her.

"This is Jamaican rum punch Nellie!" Dee said sounding serious. "It's made with over-proof Jamaican rum, and you don't drink!" If Dee was using that dismal tone in her voice to dissuade her from trying the rum punch, it didn't work. It never usually worked with our friend if she sets her mind to trying something, whether it be a very peppery jerk chicken, curried goat, or on this occasion, rum punch.

"I had a Jim Collins a while ago at a workmate's wedding reception," she persisted. "It wasn't that bad."

"I don't know what a Jim Collins is," I retorted, "but I don't think it can be compared with this."

"How do you make it?" she asked, opening the cupboard where the glasses were kept and taking a small tumbler out. "What else is in it beside the rum?"

"Rum, lime juice, Jamaican strawberry syrup and water," I had offered. "I can't give you proportions of each because it is a guarded family recipe handed down from one generation to the other." Nellie had chuckled as she poured a small amount into the glass just covering the bottom, and our eyes followed her every movement. She had cautiously taken a sip.

"Hmmmmm!" she had said, smiling at us. "It tastes good. It really does!" She had finished what was in the glass and was pouring some more into it. This time the glass was half full.

"I don't think you should have anymore, Nellie." I had coaxed. "That stuff tastes sweet, but it can creep up on you if you're not used to it."

Ignoring my pleas, she had emptied the contents of the glass into her mouth, put the glass in the sink, and moved to the sofa once again. We had followed her into the living room.

"Are you alright?" Dee had asked, for although she looked okay, we were a bit concerned.

"I'm fine," she waved us off. "Will you two sit down and stop worrying? I just had a taste of the stuff, for crying out loud!"

"You don't know what a 'taste of the stuff' can do," I had thought, remembering my first experience with it that Christmas day when I was fourteen. We had had visitors as was usual for the season, and rum punch was being served as was also usual.

I had never been really interested in trying rum punch before, but everyone had seemed to be enjoying it, so I had asked to taste Aunt Maude's. It had tasted so good that I had poured out half a glass for myself. I had ended up sleeping through Christmas dinner and all the merry makings that went on.

When I finally surfaced late Boxing Day, it was in the company of a terrible headache. After that, even if I made it at Christmas time for my guests, I never touched it except for the occasional sip.

"....and I forgot to mail them, so I decided to bring them over. I received yours by the way, thanks." Nellie was rummaging through her purse.

"What did you forget to mail?" I had asked, having missed the trend of her conversation.

"My Christmas cards to you both," she answered, closing her purse and heading for the door.

"Where are you going?" Dee asked, following her to the door.

"I must have left the cards in my car. I'll go get them and come back." Before we could protest she was at the elevator and on it.

While she was gone, Dee and I had voiced our uneasiness about the drink she had taken. We were debating whether one of us should offer to drive her home when our door buzzer went. Dee answered it.

"Would someone come down to the lobby right away please?" It was the voice of the building's superintendent. "Your friend had an accident." He sounded upset.

We had both dashed through the doorway leaving the door ajar, and bounded down the stairs to the lobby. Nellie was sitting in one of the chairs holding her face in her hands. The superintendent was standing over her like a mother hen, asking over and over if she was alright.

"What happened?" I had asked, going over to assist my friend.

"I think I did too good a job polishing that wall and door," He pointed to the glass wall and entrance door to the building with his eyes. "Your friend walked into it."

"Oh my goodness!" Dee and I uttered in unison as Nellie raised her head and we viewed the damage. There was a small abrasion on the top of her nose and lower lip, and she appeared a bit shaken. There was evidence that her nose had bled a little.

I left her with Dee and went back to the

apartment for our coats and an ice-pack. when I returned to the lobby the superintendent was gone and Nellie looked more composed. She was trying to joke about it. I handed Dee the ice-pack and her coat and said " Put this on her forehead Dee. I'll bring my car 'round. We're taking her to Emergency."

"You don't need to do that Lynette, I feel better ..." Her voice trailed off in the distance as I rode the elevator to the underground garage to get my car.

Dee and I had trouble convincing her that she needed to be seen by a doctor, but finally she had succumbed to our coaxing.

On our way to the hospital, Nellie had been trying to figure out how she could have walked into a glass wall thinking it was an open

doorway. No one had mentioned the rum punch until she did just now.

* * * * *

A nurse came to take her to the x-ray Department. Dee tagged along.

"Just to ascertain that there are no broken bones," the doctor had said assuringly. "I hope to God there aren't any," I said in my mind, "her husband would never forgive us."

"John!" I said aloud, realizing that we had forgotten to call him. "I'll call John and tell him what happened," I shouted at their receding forms. Dee turned and waved consent and I went to the pay phone.

He accepted the news well I thought, and in fifteen minutes was in the Emergency Room getting a first hand account of the accident from

125

his bruised, swollen-faced mate.

"I'll have to put a leash on you from now on to keep you out of trouble," John said smiling as he kissed his wife gently on the lips.

"Either that or a muzzle over my mouth so I won't be tempted to taste trouble," she replied. They kissed again and I looked away thinking of how tender they were with each other.

Half an hour later we saw them off. Nellie lay supine in the passenger seat half asleep from the effects of the pain killers she had been given. John shouted "Merry Christmas," as he drove away.

"Merry Christmas!" we shouted back.

"And I hope to God we don't hear any more talk of Christmas cards and rum punch," Dee muttered to herself.

"Amen!" I said, and we went to get my car.

Linda M. Brissett

Christmas Is In The Heart

It is that time of year again when people all over Christendom celebrate in various ways, the festival called Christmas. Christmas, Xmas, Noel. But what is Christmas?

Some may say that it is the time of year when Christians everywhere celebrate the anniversary of the birth of Jesus, the Saviour of the world, who made His humble entrance in a stable among farm animals, in a far off place called Bethlehem. Though He was the Son of God, the King of heaven and earth, He waived all His glory in favour of humility, in order to show His ineffable love for mankind.

With this in mind, many people regard Christmas as a time to show love. Love for families, friends, neighbours and people with whom they work. Some of this love hopefully will spill over to include strangers they come in contact with, and even those whom they consider to be their enemies.

Many regard Christmas as a time for taking that well earned, and longed for vacation, maybe on the snowy slopes of the Swiss Alps or the Canadian Rockies; or a fishing trip to Bermuda; a sun-splash week in the Caribbean; or just sitting at home by the hearth, sipping hot cider, and dreaming of a white Christmas.

To others, Christmas is a time for going

on a shopping spree, buying for relatives, friends and themselves. After all aren't all these things what Christmas is about?

No! Not for the victims of economical recessions of Christmases past and present.

These are very lean times. Times of weariness, worry, and want for many Canadians who have become victims of the prolonged recession that has been plaguing the country for almost four years, and from which there doesn't seem to be any escape, even at Christmas time.

Many people (some of whom are from middle class families who have joined the ranks of the poor), will find themselves in lines at soup kitchens and food banks across the country. Unable to go on any kind of shopping spree be it for food clothes or toys. They will try to survive on what little they get from Social Services, and what, if any, handouts that may be forth coming from caring relatives and friends, some of whom may be just a step ahead of being in the same boat with them.

Christmas for these people will be a time of sadness, disappointment and frustration, if they give in to these feeling, and give up on life. For them it will come down to the crux of the matter. It is not **WHAT**, but **WHERE** Christmas is, and how it can be recognised.

Christmas is not in the stores with the biggest and brightest trees. Nor is it in the oven housing the largest, most succulent turkey or ham. It is not in the amount of gifts one finds under his tree on Christmas morning. Nor is it at the grand ball in the large house on the hill.

Christmas is the love and kindness shown to the needy, the indigent, the unfortunate, the homeless. The families of the steel and health workers and civil servants who have been made redundant, and are rapidly loosing hope; by those of us who can help, if only by donating to food banks, or giving what we can to such worthwhile organizations as the Christmas Tree Of Hope.

Christmas is in the hearts of those who haven't much themselves, but are eager and willing to share with those who have not. And Christmas is in the hearts of those who have not, yet to find themselves alive and well and free, in this country, at Christmas time, is more than they could hope for. It is joy unspeakable. A joy they are ever thankful for.

Christmas is **LOVE**, and **CARING**, and **SHARING**, and all of this comes from the heart.

Illustrations

About the Author:

Linda M. Brissett is a Registered Nurse and Certified Midwife who for 28 years worked in Neonatology at Henderson General Hospital in Hamilton. She is a member of the Canadian Authors Association and The Canadian Poetry Association. As a member of the Board of Directors of The Afro-Canadian Caribbean Association of Hamilton and District, she is also an active member of The Jamaica Foundation, a charitable organization and a member of the church choir.

In Hamilton, Ontario, Linda lives with her husband Louis and their son Ian.

Other publications are her three books of poetry - "In Fields of Dream and Other Poems - "Sunshine in the Shadows" and "Give Us This Day". She contributed to the anthology "The First Time" and also to "Ingots" a sesqui-centennial poetry anthology of Hamilton which was published in May 1996. She is published regularly in "Authors" and the "Bulletin".